Perdidos en el Camino del Inca

Serie
Aventura joven

Título
Perdidos en el Camino del Inca

Autores
Elvira Sancho y Jordi Surís

Coordinación editorial
Jaime Corpas

Redacción
Montse Belver

Diseño e ilustración de cubierta
Àngel Viola

Diseño interior y maquetación
Jasmina Car y Óscar García Ortega

Ilustraciones
Roger Zanni

Material auditivo
Voz:
Elena Menacho

Grabación y edición CD:
Blind Records

ISBN: 978-84-8443-544-0

Depósito Legal: M-12450-2009

Impreso en España por Raro

difusión
Centro de
Investigación y
Publicaciones
de Idiomas, S. L

C/ Trafalgar, 10, entlo. 1ª
08010 Barcelona
Tel. (+34) 93 268 03 00
Fax (+34) 93 310 33 40
editorial@difusion.com

www.difusion.com

AVENTURA JOVEN

Perdidos en el Camino del Inca

ELVIRA SANCHO
JORDI SURÍS

difusión

PRESENTACIÓN

La serie **Aventura joven** narra las aventuras que vive un grupo de amigos adolescentes: Mónica, Guillermo, Laura, Sergio y Martín. A través de sus historias, los vas a ir conociendo y, al mismo tiempo, vas a descubrir muchos aspectos del mundo hispano.

A lo largo de la lectura de **Perdidos en el Camino del Inca**, hay una serie de notas que te van a ayudar a comprender mejor el texto y te van a explicar algunas interesantes cuestiones culturales, referentes al Perú.

Recuerda que para entender un texto, no es imprescindible conocer el significado de cada una de las palabras: intenta comprender el texto en su totalidad y disfruta al máximo de la lectura.

Esta novela va acompañada de un CD audio (que contiene además archivos mp3) con el que podrás escuchar la historia grabada por una voz peruana.

«Después de la lectura», te proponemos una serie de actividades. Te van a permitir comprobar si has entendido el texto y te van a ayudar a incorporar nuevo vocabulario o a reflexionar sobre los temas de actualidad que preocupan a los jóvenes. Al final de la novela, hemos añadido las soluciones a esas actividades.

¡Disfruta de la historia!

CAPÍTULO 1

—Guille, ¿tú llevas cámara de fotos? —pregunta Mónica entrando en la habitación de los chicos.

—No, pero Sergio lleva la suya —contesta Guille—. Y tú, ¿estás contenta de ir a Machu Picchu?

—Sí. Mis padres me han hablado mucho del Camino del Inca... Y también quiero visitar Cusco, a la vuelta. Guille, ¿te encuentras bien? Estás un poco blanco...

—Sí, estoy un poco mareado, es por la altura[1].

Guille y Mónica son amigos. El chico es un poco gordo y pelirrojo. Tiene dieciséis años pero parece más joven.

—¡Hola! —Laura, una chica alta y rubia, entra en la habitación—. ¿Estáis listos?

—Sí —Guille se pone en la espalda su mochila grande. Luego, coge otra más pequeña. Los chicos salen al pasillo.

Desde la ventana del pasillo se ve Cusco. Laura se para a mirar. Están en un hostal[2] en el barrio de San Blas, uno de los más antiguos de la ciudad. Es un barrio de artesanos y artistas. Hay muchos talleres y tiendas pequeñas.

—Al volver de Machu Picchu quiero ir a todas esas tiendecitas —dice Mónica a Laura.

Martín sube corriendo por la escalera.

—Nuria dice que llevemos algo de abrigo.

—Pero si no hace frío...

[1] **altura:** Cusco está a unos 3500 metros de altura, lo que en algunas personas provoca el llamado «mal de altura» o «soroche». Los síntomas del mal de altura son: dolor de cabeza, mareos, trastornos estomacales y cansancio. Puede combatirse con pastillas, ejercicios de respiración o mate.

[2] **hostal:** alojamiento normalmente más barato y personal que un hotel, aunque sin sus comodidades. La palabra se utiliza principalmente en medios rurales.

—Es que por la noche refresca.

—Yo me llevo una chaqueta —contesta Laura, bajando las escaleras.

—Dentro de diez minutos en recepción —dice Nuria desde abajo. Nuria es la tutora[3] de la clase. Es una mujer simpática, de pelo largo y castaño.

—Vale, vale... —contestan los chicos.

—¿Tenéis todo?, ¿cámaras?, ¿linternas?, ¿crema de sol?, ¿cantimplora? —pregunta Nuria.

Los alumnos de la clase de cuarto de ESO del instituto Gaudí de Barcelona, están en Perú de viaje de fin de curso[4]. Dos profesores acompañan a los diecisiete alumnos: Nuria, la profesora de Ciencias Naturales y tutora de la clase, y Jaime Crespo, el profesor de Arte y Literatura. Desde España han viajado a Lima, la capital de Perú, y desde allí a Cusco.

El plan es hacer un *trekking* de dos días hasta Machu Picchu y después visitar Cusco y sus alrededores.

Ahora los estudiantes están reunidos en la recepción del hostal. Las mochilas están en un rincón. Nuria, la profesora, habla con un hombre bajo y moreno, con el pelo largo, recogido en una trenza.

—Lo siento, es muy amable, pero ya tenemos guías —dice Nuria, señalando a unos jóvenes que hablan con el dueño del hostal.

Mónica se acerca a Nuria.

—¿Vamos a ver las ruinas de Brutthalva[5]?

El hombre moreno del pelo largo mira a Mónica fijamente.

—No es una buena idea —dice con una sonrisa. Mónica puede ver que tiene un diente de oro—. Están lejos del camino y no son interesantes.

---

3 **tutora**: profesora encargada de un curso. Normalmente imparte clase y se encarga de los problemas de los alumnos y de su relación con otros profesores y las familias.

4 **viaje fin de curso**: en España es costumbre entre los estudiantes al finalizar el ciclo de ESO (Educación Secundaria Obligatoria) o de Bachillerato realizar un viaje.

5 **ruinas de Brutthalva**: en el camino del Machu Picchu se encuentran gran cantidad de ruinas de esta índole. Bruthalva es un nombre ficticio.

—¿No? —dice Mónica sorprendida. No le gusta el hombre—.

—Yo conozco el lugar, señorita —el hombre sonríe. Quiere parecer simpático, pero es desagradable—. Además, esta zona es peligrosa, está maldita...

—Pero...

—Hay otras más interesantes...

Jaime, el profesor, se acerca:

—Los autobuses están fuera. Podemos marcharnos.

—¿Quién era ese hombre? —pregunta Laura acercándose a su amiga.

—Dice que es guía. Oye, tiene un diente de oro...

—Es un hombre muy raro.

— ... y dice que las ruinas de Brutthalva están malditas.

—Pero hay muchas por el camino, ¿no?

—¿Y qué? —dice Mónica enfadada—. Yo quiero visitar estas porque hace poco que las han descubierto. Además no soy supersticiosa⁶.

El autobús avanza por las calles estrechas y empinadas⁷ del barrio de San Blas. Los chicos están contentos.

—Mirad, esta es la parroquia de San Blas —dice Mónica señalando una iglesia blanca con las escaleras y una torre de piedra.

—La visitaremos al volver.

—Sí.

—¡Es muy bonita...! —exclama Mónica.

—¿Es inca? —pregunta Raúl, un compañero de clase, que se sienta a su lado.

—No, es de estilo barroco pero está construida sobre un santuario inca. Era para el dios Illapa⁸. La mayoría de edificios...

—Mónica, ¿te has estudiado toda la historia del Perú?

—Es tan interesante... Y, mirad, esta es la plaza de Armas. Y ahí está la catedral. ¿No es increíble? —Mónica sonríe.

---

6 supersticiosa: persona que cree que determinados sucesos traen buena o mala suerte.

7 empinadas: muy altas.

8 Illapa: para los incas, el dios de la lluvia, el rayo y el trueno.

Los chicos miran delante de ellos. Es una plaza grande con zonas ajardinadas. En medio hay una fuente rodeada de césped donde algunos jóvenes están sentados. Al otro lado está la catedral que señala Mónica.

—Es preciosa —dice Jaime, el profesor que está de pie en el pasillo del autobús—. Está construida con piedras de un templo inca. Antes allí, había un palacio.

Los chicos siguen admirando la ciudad. Detrás de los edificios y tejados rojos de las casas se ven las montañas andinas.

Es agosto, la época seca, y se puede ver un cielo azul con muy pocas nubes.

—¡No puedo creer que estamos en la capital inca! —dice Laura contenta.

—¡Y que vamos a Machu Picchu! —continúa Mónica emocionada.

—¿Cómo se llama el próximo pueblo? —pregunta Martín mirando el mapa.

Martín es un chico delgado, atlético y con el pelo castaño y rizado. Lleva pantalones vaqueros, una camiseta y una gorra roja. Es muy amigo de Sergio, Laura, Mónica y Guille.

—Urubamba, ¿no? —dice Sergio.

—¿Urubamba no es el nombre del río?

—Y de la provincia, y de la montaña, y también de un pueblo —explica David, uno de los guías.

—¡Vaya lío[9]! —dice Guille.

De repente se oye un sonido suave.

—¡Ah! ¡Compraste una ocarina[10]! —exclama David mirando a Ana, una chica que está haciendo sonar el instrumento.

—Sí. Es muy popular aquí, ¿verdad?

—Claro.

—Es bonita y suena bien. Yo también he comprado una... —dice un chico de gafas que está sentado al otro lado del pasillo.

9 **lío**: en lenguaje coloquial algo que resulta complicado.

10 **ocarina**: pequeño instrumento musical de viento hecho de barro, de madera o plástico y, en algunos casos más raros, de vegetales y de frutas. Tiene su origen en la civilización Quechua.

—Primero pasamos por Chincheros, ¿verdad? —pregunta Mónica desde el asiento de delante.

—Sí —contesta David, que se sienta cerca de los amigos.

David es estudiante y en la temporada turística trabaja de guía. Aníbal es el otro guía. También es estudiante.

—¿Paramos en Urubamba?

—No Guille, solo la veremos desde el ómnibus. Vamos directamente hasta Piscacucho.

—¿Esto es el kilómetro 82 de la vía férrea[11]?

—Sí, ahí es donde empezamos el *trekking*.

—¿Cuántas horas tenemos que caminar hoy? —pregunta Guille.

—Siete.

—¿Siete?

—Pero paramos en Miskay para comer —dice Martín sonriendo. A Guille no le gusta mucho caminar.

—Además nos llevan las mochilas.

Con el grupo van dos porteadores[12] quechuas[13] para llevar las mochilas con los sacos de dormir. Los profesores y los chicos solo tienen que llevar una pequeña mochila con las cámaras, la cantimplora y una chaqueta o poncho[14].

El autobús sale de Cusco y sigue la carretera. Al cabo de un rato pasan por Urubamba. El pueblo es grande y plano; está en el valle, al pie de la cordillera del Urubamba. Después de pasar por unos cuantos pueblecitos más, llegan finalmente a Piscacucho.

11 **vía férrea**: vía del tren.

12 **porteadores**: personas que acompañan a los turistas en las excursiones y les llevan su equipaje a cambio de dinero.

13 **quechua**: es el nombre de una cultura, de una lengua y de los habitantes que vivieron en los Andes centrales de Sudamérica. Más de 8 millones de personas hablan actualmente la lengua quechua principalmente en Ecuador, Perú y Bolivia.

14 **poncho**: prenda de abrigo que consiste en una manta, cuadrada o rectangular, de lana, que tiene en el centro una abertura para pasar la cabeza. Es una prenda de origen andino.

CAPÍTULO 2

—¡Ya hemos llegado! —exclama Laura contenta.

Los dos guías y los chicos bajan del autobús.

—¿Estáis todos bien? —pregunta Nuria sonriendo.

—Yo estoy un poco mareado[1] —dice Guille.

—Nuria, Marta también está mareada —dice Ana.

—¿Has traído pastillas para el mareo? —pregunta Nuria mirando a la chica.

—Sí. Ahora me la tomo.

—Es la altura. El cuerpo necesita tiempo para adaptarse.

Los chicos miran el paisaje verde a su alrededor con las montañas al fondo. Otros autobuses llenos de turistas aparcan cerca. También van a hacer *trekking*.

David y Aníbal saludan a dos hombres que esperan al lado del autobús.

—Manuel, Pedro... ¿cómo van?

—Bien, nomás[2].

—Vengan y les presento al grupo.

Algunos chicos aún están bajando del autobús y recogiendo sus mochilas. David se acerca a Nuria y Jaime:

—Estos son Pedro y Manuel, nuestros porteadores.

—Hola, encantada.

—Nuria, ¿qué hacemos con las mochilas? —pregunta Mónica, que se acerca con una mochila muy grande en la mano.

—De momento podéis dejarlas en el suelo —responde Nuria, que sigue hablando con los porteadores.

— Démela nomás, yo la pongo con las otras.

---

1 **mareado:** persona que sufre mareo; una indisposición en la que uno se siente débil, con pérdida de equilibrio y a veces dolor de estómago y/o nauseas.

2 **nomás:** solo, únicamente. Se utiliza también para dar énfasis.

David se acerca a Mónica y le coge la mochila.

—¡No, no, la puedo llevar yo! —exclama Mónica.

El chico sonríe divertido:

—¡Si quiere...!. Pero es la mía y pesa mucho.

Mónica mira la mochila. Se ha equivocado. La mochila no es la suya. Se pone colorada[3] y mira al chico que le sigue sonriendo.

—Ah, perdón... Sí, toma... gracias —dice.

Mónica vuelve al autobús a buscar su mochila.

—¿Vienen con nosotros? —dice Laura señalando a los dos porteadores.

—Sí. Ellos llevan todo el equipaje.

—¡Qué bien! —dice Ana, una chica con el pelo largo y rizado.

Los dos guías hablan con Jaime. David es bajo, moreno y delgado, y lleva gafas redondas. Aníbal es más alto y fuerte. También es moreno. Hablan con el profesor y le explican la ruta sobre un mapa.

—Chicos, poneos crema solar y *spray* antimosquitos —aconseja Nuria.

—Yo tengo, ¿alguien necesita? —pregunta Ana.

El grupo empieza a caminar.

—Mira, vamos hacia allí, ¿no? —dice Guille señalando unas montañas azules al fondo.

—Sí, hay mucha niebla allí.

—Sí, en cambio aquí hace calor.

—¡Empezamos el camino Sagrado, chicos! —explica Aníbal.

Los chicos, los profesores y los guías y porteadores caminan en grupos de tres o cuatro. Siguen un camino de piedras y hierbas.

—¿Tenemos que subir esta montaña? —pregunta Guillermo.

—Esto no es una montaña Guille —dice Sergio—. ¡Solo es una cuesta[4]!

—¿Cuántas escaleras hay?

—Todo el camino son escaleras —bromea Aníbal.

---

3 **ponerse colorado/a**: cuando la cara se tiñe de color rojo a causa de vergüenza o timidez.

4 **cuesta**: terreno en desnivel.

—¡Solo es un día, Guille! —le anima Mónica.

Mónica está contenta de que los dos guías caminen con ellos.

—¡Dos días! —corrige Guillermo.

—Bueno, pero solo una noche. Y mañana visitamos Machu Picchu. ¿Sabes cuánto dura el camino tradicional? ¡Cuatro días!

—¡Y hay otros que duran doce! —exclama Martín. El chico está contento porque le gusta mucho caminar por las montañas.

Los chicos siguen andando. Ahora hay muy poca vegetación.

—Esto ¿no es..., no es... Choquesuysuy? —exclama Mónica excitada.

David la mira con interés.

—¡Claro!

Los chicos miran hacia unas ruinas un poco lejos a la izquierda del camino.

—¿Qué es? —pregunta Raúl.

—Son unas rui... —empieza a explicar David, pero Mónica lo interrumpe.

—Es un conjunto arqueológico religioso. Está cerca de Machu Picchu y era famoso por sus fuentes... —de pronto mira al guía.

—¡Perdona! —dice.

David sonríe divertido.

—Continúe, continúe, lo hace muy bien.

—¡Mónica es una enciclopedia viviente! —dice Martín.

—Perfecto, así puede ayudarme. —David ríe y continúa explicando la historia de Choquesuysuy.

—¡Un momento! Voy a tomar algunas fotos —Sergio saca la cámara.

—¡Oh! Desde aquí es perfecto —Sergio toma más fotos.

Laura bebe agua de su cantimplora.

—¿Estas son las ruinas que quieres ver? —le pregunta después a Mónica.

—No. Las ruinas que yo quiero ver están cerca de Wiñaywayna. Se han descubierto hace poco, pero parece que no están en el camino.

—Vamos a preguntar a David si podemos ir a verlas. ¡David!

—¿Sí?

—Mónica quiere ver unas ruinas que han descubierto hace poco.

—¿Cuáles? —pregunta el guía.

—Unas que están cerca de Wayñawamba, ¿cómo se llaman Mónica?

—Las de Brutthalva, las que están cerca de Wiñaywayna.

David mira a Mónica, sorprendido.

—¿Y cómo sabes tú eso? —le pregunta a la chica.

Mónica se pone colorada.

—Er... mis padres están suscritos a «Viajes exóticos del Mundo», una revista, ¿sabes? Y hablan de estas ruinas. ¿Sabes cuáles son?

—Sí, las conozco. Un profesor de mi universidad estuvo en la expedición[5] que las encontró...

—¿Ah, sí?

—Sí, pero todavía no están abiertas al público.

—Un guía en el hotel nos dijo que están malditas —sigue Mónica.

—¿Malditas? —David ríe—. Hay mucha gente supersticiosa aquí. Pero es extraño, porque casi nadie las conoce. ¿Quién se lo dijo?

—No sé, un señor en el hotel. Un hombre de cabello largo y un diente de oro.

—¡Ah! —dice David pensativo.

—¿Podemos ir cuando lleguemos a Wiñaywayna? —pregunta Laura.

—No, entonces ya es tarde y oscurece rápido.

—¡Oh¡ ¡Me encantaría verlas! —insiste Mónica.

—¡Pero si hay muchas ruinas! —exclama Guille.

—Esto es distinto. Estas aún no las conoce nadie.

—Seguro que todavía no se puede ver nada —insiste Guillermo.

—¡Lo que pasa es que tú no quieres caminar!

—No, no es caminar. ¡Es el calor! Y... ¿cuándo paramos para comer?

---

5 **expedición:** excursión colectiva a alguna ciudad o lugar con un fin científico, artístico o deportivo.

Todos ríen. Guille siempre tiene hambre.

—El chico tiene razón —dice Aníbal—. Es hora de tomar un *snack*. Podemos parar aquí. Hay buena vista[6].

Cuando continúan la excursión, Mónica y David caminan juntos hablando animadamente sobre la historia del imperio inca.

—¿Falta mucho para Wiñaywayna? —pregunta Nuria después de unas horas de camino.

—No, justo allá —contesta Aníbal.— Miren allá.

El guía señala la montaña a la izquierda del río.

Desde donde están se ven grupos de casas de piedra entre grandes terrazas[7] en círculo.

—¡Qué increíble! —exclama Nuria.

—El nombre significa «siempre joven» —añade David—. Y se cree que además de agricultura se cultivaban flores, en las terrazas.

—¡Es precioso! —Laura mira las ruinas con admiración.

—Allá es donde vamos a acampar —dice David.

—¿En las ruinas? —exclama Ana, la chica de la ocarina, horrorizada.

—No —David ríe—. Dormiremos en el albergue[8].

—¡Ah, vale!

David y Aníbal se han alejado un poco y hablan.

Mónica y Sergio se han parado y miran el paisaje.

—¿Qué te ha dicho David? ¿Podemos ver las ruinas que tú quieres? —pregunta Sergio—. A mí me gustaría tomar fotos.

—Mmm... no sé. Dice que normalmente los grupos no se dividen por si hay algún problema.

—¿Qué problemas? —pregunta Martín.

—No sé...

---

6 **buena vista:** paisaje que se ve desde un punto y es bonito o interesante.

7 **terraza:** grandes escalones construidos sobre las laderas o montañas, normalmente con el objetivo de cultivar en ellos.

8 **albergue:** alojamiento, particularmente pensado para estancias cortas y para promover el intercambio cultural entre jóvenes de distintos países. Suele ser barato.

Cuando están llegando a Wiñaywayna, David se acerca a los chicos.

—He hablado con Aníbal. Está de acuerdo. Él seguirá con el grupo grande...

—¡Bien...! —exclaman Mónica y Laura.

—Y nosotros iremos a ver las ruinas de Bruttalva.

—¡Vale!

—Nos tendremos que levantar muy tempranito —añade David.

—¿A qué hora?

—A las cinco de la mañana. Nos volveremos a reunir con el grupo en Machu Picchu.

—De acuerdo. ¡Bien!

—Pero con una condición —David sonríe y levanta el dedo—, vuestros profesores tienen que estar de acuerdo.

—Ya les he preguntado... —dice Mónica—. Dicen que sí.

—Entonces, ¡está hecho⁹!

Mónica mira a David con una gran sonrisa.

—¿Quién va a ir?

—¡Yo! —dice Mónica levantando el dedo.

—Yo también —exclama Sergio.

Laura y Martín también se apuntan.

—Nosotros también —dicen Raúl y Ana.

—De acuerdo. Ustedes seis.

—Guillermo, ¿tú no te apuntas? —pregunta Mónica.

—No... es que estoy cansado.

Están llegando al albergue. Es tarde, pronto se hará de noche.

—David, el guía... te mira mucho, ¿no? —dice Laura a Mónica cuando se quedan solas.

—¿Qué dices?

—Que le gustas.

Mónica se pone colorada.

---

9 **está hecho:** en lenguaje coloquial, está arreglado, estamos de acuerdo para hacer algo.

—Y a ti te gusta él —sigue Laura.

—¿Y a ti quién te lo ha dicho?

—Vamos, se te ve lejos. Además, hacéis una pareja perfecta. ¡Podéis vivir en una biblioteca! —añade riendo.

Mónica le da un empujón. Parece enfadada, pero no lo está. Está muy contenta.

—Creo que va a llover —dice Jaime mirando unas nubes negras—. ¡Venga, venga, un poco más de prisa!

—Sí, chicos, ánimo —dice Nuria mirando al cielo.

De repente el aire se ha vuelto frío. Cuando entran en el pueblo, está oscureciendo.

CAPÍTULO 3

—Eh, Laura, despierta —Mónica toca el brazo a su amiga que duerme a su lado.

—¿Ya es la hora? ¿Ya son las cinco?

—Sí, Martín ya se ha levantado.

Están en el albergue de Wiñaywayna. Los chicos duermen juntos en una sala grande.

—¡Hola! —Martín se ha acercado a las chicas— ¿Preparadas?

—Sí —contestan Mónica y Laura.

—David está en la cocina —dice el chico—. Nos está preparando té, café y galletas.

—¡Qué bien!

Desde la cocina se siente el olor del café.

Sergio también se ha despertado. Se pone las gafas y se levanta.

—¡Hola! —dice acercándose a ellos.

—¿Os vais ya? —Guillermo se ha despertado y mira a sus amigos desde la cama.

—Sí, nos vamos enseguida.

—¡Buenos días! —dice Raúl acercándose al grupo—. Nos vemos en la cocina.

—¡Vale! ¿Seguro que no quieres venir, Guille? —pregunta Mónica.

—Segurísimo —Guille se vuelve a estirar— ¡Hasta luego...!

Jaime, el profesor, está en la cocina con David, el guía, y Raúl. Quiere despedir a los chicos.

—Hasta luego —les dice—. Nos vemos en Machu Picchu.

Seguramente nosotros llegaremos antes, ¿verdad, David? —pregunta Ana, que también va a la excursión.

—Sí. Creo que sí, las ruinas no están muy lejos del camino y los otros se van a levantar más tarde.

—Bueno, adiós —dice Jaime—. Y si es interesante, ¡tomad fotos!

El pequeño grupo sale del albergue y empieza a caminar. A esta hora todavía es de noche y hace frío.

—¿Está muy lejos? —pregunta Martín.

—No, a unas dos horas —contesta David.

El camino empieza a subir. Se está haciendo de día. A lo lejos se ven las altas montañas. Delante de ellos empieza a haber niebla.

—¿Qué hacemos? —pregunta Raúl.

—Es normal la neblina a estas horas pero pronto desaparecerá —contesta David sacando una brújula de su mochila.

El grupo continúa caminando entre la niebla. El camino es estrecho, pero está bien marcado y es fácil de seguir.

Después de caminar dos horas, Mónica está impaciente.

—Ya debemos estar cerca, ¿no? —pregunta.

—Sí. Quizás este camino no es el correcto... —contesta David.

—¿Sabes volver? —pregunta Ana, asustada.

Los chicos están un poco preocupados.

De pronto, entre la niebla se oyen unas voces. El grupo se para a escuchar. Sí, son voces. También se oyen unas risas de hombre.

—Debe ser otro grupo —dice Ana contenta.

—¿Tú crees? Estamos fuera de la ruta —dice Martín.

—Tal vez van a las mismas excavaciones que nosotros, ¿no? —dice Laura.

—Silencio —dice David preocupado. Luego continúa en voz baja—. No pueden ser turistas. Esas ruinas no son conocidas, no están en ninguna ruta.

Ahora las voces se oyen más cerca. Una voz de hombre dice:

—Vamos más rápido o no vamos a llegar nunca.

Mónica escucha con atención. Esta voz... ya la ha oído antes..., pero, ¿dónde?

Las voces se alejan.

Poco después la niebla desaparece. Se puede ver el magnífico paisaje andino delante de sus ojos.

David ahora camina seguro.

—Estamos cerca —dice David—. Creo que deben estar por allá —añade señalando en frente.

Cuando llegan a una explanada, Mónica exclama.

—Sí, ¡mirad!

—Sí, es aquí... —dice David.

Delante de ellos se ve un muro de un metro de altura en forma circular. Desde allí, otros muros irregulares más bajos y un agujero de unos tres por cuatro metros. Al final hay un agujero de un metro más o menos y unas escaleras que bajan.

Mónica, Laura, Ana y Raúl se acercan corriendo.

—¡Vamos a entrar! —gritan.

—¿Se puede entrar? —pregunta Sergio a David.

—Es extraño —dice David, preocupado.

—¿Qué es extraño? —pregunta Martín.

—Normalmente están precintadas.

—¿Precintadas?

—Sí, cerradas con una valla o una cinta para indicar que no están abiertas al público. Es lo que hacen las expediciones oficiales cuando las encuentran. Se llevan lo más valioso y las precintan hasta que tienen el dinero para arreglarlas.

—Pero, ¿por qué?

—Porque todavía hay material valioso dentro. A veces los huaqueros se lo llevan para venderlo.

—¿¿Hua-qué ?? —pregunta Martín.

—Huaqueros, ladrones.

—Ladrones que se llevan ruinas y las venden —explica Sergio que ha oído hablar de los huaqueros.

—Sí. En Perú hay muchísimas huacas como estas. En estos lugares normalmente se encuentran joyas, estatuas y otros objetos muy valiosos por su antigüedad.

—Claro, los tesoros incas.

—Sí. Son de época inca o preinca.

David, Sergio y Martín han llegado a las ruinas.

—Vamos a entrar por ahí —dice David.

Los chicos pasan por un agujero de un metro que entra en las rocas y bajan unos escalones.

—¡¡¡Uauu!!! Mirad esto —David está emocionado.

—¿Qué es? —pregunta Ana mirando una cabeza de piedra tallada de una forma muy tosca¹ en la misma roca.

—Es la cabeza del Inti, el dios del sol. Y siempre va acompañada de la de la luna —David mira a su alrededor.

—¡Qué grave! —exclama de pronto enfadado.

—¿Qué? —pregunta Mónica sorprendida.

—¡Se han llevado la de Mama Quilla, seguro! —David toca con las manos una roca tallada recientemente.

—¿Qué se han llevado?

—Los huaqueros se han llevado una estatua entera. Mama Quilla es la hermana y la esposa del dios Inti. Esta diosa, representada por la Luna, acompañaba a Inti...

—¿Y cómo sabes que han sido los huaqueros? Tal vez han sido los de la expedición —interrumpe Martín.

—No. Ellos se llevan los objetos pero nunca rompen las rocas.

—Las voces... —empieza Laura.

—¿Qué voces? —pregunta Martín.

—Las que hemos oído hace poco... —dice Laura.

—¡Ah!, las voces en la niebla...

—¿Han sido ellos? —pregunta Raúl.

—No lo sé... —dice David, que continúa enfadado.

Cuando salen de nuevo fuera, el sol empieza a estar alto en el cielo. Los chicos están impresionados.

Mónica está emocionada. Ha tocado las piedras de dentro de las ruinas, y las estatuas cubiertas de piedras y vegetación. Y ahora toca las rocas de fuera. Viaja con la imaginación muchos años atrás, a la época de los incas.

---

1 **tosca:** hecho con poco cuidado o con materiales poco valiosos. En el texto: hecho de forma rudimentaria, primitiva.

David sale el último de las ruinas. Está callado. Piensa en los huaqueros. Finalmente empieza a caminar.

—Tenemos que seguir el camino o no vamos a alcanzar el grupo —dice impaciente.

—¡Vale! —dice Mónica mirando a las ruinas. —¡Adiós, ruinas!

Los chicos empiezan a caminar.

Mónica hace preguntas a David sobre la cueva y los incas. Pero David no la escucha. Está preocupado.

—¡Qué tonto soy! —exclama de pronto Sergio.

—¿Qué pasa?

—¡No he hecho fotos!

—¿No has hecho fotos? —Mónica parece decepcionada— ¡Vamos a volver!

—No podemos volver, es muy tarde —dice David.

—Vale, vosotros seguid, yo voy en un momento —dice Sergio.

—¿Sabrá volver?

—Sólo tengo que seguir el camino, ¿no?

A David no le gusta la idea:

—¿Y si se pierde?

—No, no te preocupes.

Sergio corre hacia las ruinas. Los otros chicos continúan caminando.

Después de un rato, David se para. Sergio todavía no ha vuelto.

—¿Crees que se habrá perdido? —pregunta Laura preocupada. David la mira.

—Solo hay este camino —dice. Quiere parecer tranquilo pero también está preocupado.

—Sí, pero es extraño, tanto tiempo para hacer unas fotos... —dice Laura.

—Seguramente está haciendo fotos de todas las piedras, ya sabes como es Sergio —dice Martín.

El grupo sigue caminando en silencio. Ahora el sol ya está alto y empieza a hacer calor.

—Paramos aquí —dice David—. Vamos a tomar un *snack*, a ver si llega.

A todos les parece buena idea. Se sientan en el suelo y sacan sus bocadillos.

Sergio corre hasta las ruinas con la cámara en la mano. Cuando llega al muro, empieza a hacer fotos. Primero saca unas fotos desde fuera. Luego entra en el interior y fotografía la estatua del Inti. Después, el resto de las estatuas de animales talladas en las rocas como un puma, un cóndor, varias serpientes y muchas otras piezas. Las ruinas debían ser de un lugar sagrado muy importante.

Cuando está sacando la última foto, oye unas voces que vienen de fuera. «Mis amigos han venido a buscarme» piensa, sonriendo.

—¡Ahora salgo! —grita— Ya estoy terminando...

Cuando sale, unos hombres le miran sorprendidos y enfadados.

—¿Quién eres tú? y ¿qué haces aquí? —pregunta uno de ellos, que tiene el pelo negro con una trenza.

«¡Ostras, los huaqueros!» piensa el chico.

—Yo, yo... soy estudiante y... —empieza a hablar.

—¿Y por qué te has separado de tu grupo?

—¿Dónde está tu grupo?

Sergio mira a los hombres que están delante suyo. Son tres. El hombre del pelo negro con una trenza... ¿dónde lo ha visto?

Sergio está nervioso.

—Voy al Machu Picchu con mi escuela. Nosotros hemos venido a ver...

—¿Quién es «nosotros»? —dice el hombre mirando a su alrededor.

Sergio piensa rápido, tal vez es mejor no decir que hay más gente con él.

—Yo, bueno, me gustan las fotos y he venido a sacar algunas fotos.

—Pero ¿cómo sabes...?

—No importa, —le interrumpe un hombre bajo y moreno, también de pelo negro—. Dame esa cámara.

—¿Mi cámara? No —Sergio coge la cámara con fuerza.

—Vamos a llevarlo a la choza[2].

—Bueno, adiós, me voy —dice Sergio empezando a andar.

—¡Quieto! Tú no vas a ningún lado.

El hombre lo agarra por el brazo. Sergio intenta irse, pero el hombre le tuerce el brazo.

—¡He dicho que quieto!

—Y si gritas, —dice con una risa desagradable —te mato.

Sergio está asustado. ¿Son realmente los huaqueros?, ¿Qué quieren?, ¿Dónde lo van a llevar?, ¿Por qué no le han quitado la cámara?

Los hombres lo empujan por el campo hasta llegar a una choza de piedra, que está detrás de unos árboles, a unos pocos minutos de allá.

—¡Pasa! ¡Adentro! —le ordena uno de los hombres.

La choza es pequeña. El interior está a oscuras. Hay algunas piedras en el suelo.

Fuera, los hombres hablan.

—¿Qué vamos a hacer con él? —pregunta uno de ellos.

—No lo sé. Es mejor preguntar al jefe. No queremos problemas.

—¿Y si nos deshacemos de él?

—No, lo van a buscar, va a haber una investigación.

—¡Maldita sea! —exclama uno de los hombres.

Luego los hombres se alejan. Sergio se queda solo en la oscuridad. Lentamente sus ojos empiezan a ver algunas cosas. En la choza no hay ventanas, solo un pequeño agujero en el techo por donde entra un poco de luz.

A diez minutos de distancia, el pequeño grupo está tomando un *snack*.

—¡Algo no va bien! —exclama David de pronto—. Voy a volver a buscar a Sergio.

—Yo voy contigo —dice Laura.

—Y yo también... —dicen los otros chicos.

David los mira y piensa por unos momentos. Quizás es mejor no volverse a separar.

---

2 **choza**: un tipo de construcción de madera o de piedra utilizado como vivienda habitual, principalmente por pastores y gente de campo.

—¡Está bien! —dice finalmente—. De acuerdo. Vamos todos.

Caminan rápido de vuelta a las ruinas. El guía está serio y preocupado. Cuando llegan a la excavación, David se para.

—¡Un momento! ¡Silencio! —exclama.

Los chicos escuchan en silencio.

Se oyen unas voces que se acercan.

El guía y los chicos se esconden detrás de unas rocas.

CAPÍTULO 4

Desde su escondite, David y los chicos ven a tres hombres que están sacando algo de las ruinas.

—Esto pesa, ¿eh? —dice un hombre moreno y bajo, de pelo negro.

—¡Espero que nos den mucho billete¹! —le contesta su compañero, un hombre de pelo negro y una trenza. Al hablar se le ve un diente de oro.

—¡Es el guía del hotel! —exclama Mónica desde su escondite— ¿Qué hace aquí?

—Espera, agarra por aquí..... No, no, no, ¡cuidado!

—¡Menos hablar y más trabajar! —ordena un hombre alto y rubio.

—Jefe, esto pesa mucho.

—Lo quiero todo en la choza hoy... —ordena el hombre alto.

—Tranquilo, amigo —responde el hombre de la trenza y el diente de oro—. Estamos trabajando mucho. Y estas piedras pesan un montón...

—Además nadie pasa por aquí, el camino de los grupos está lejos.

—Sí, pero... ese chico. Estaba haciendo fotos ahí dentro.

—Sí, jefe. Ahora está amarradito en la choza.

— Me preocupa, Fulgencio, me preocupa. Nadie tiene que vernos.

—Tienen a Sergio —exclama Laura, llorando al oír a los hombres.

—Seguro que no lo tienen lejos... —David está muy preocupado.

---

1 mucho billete: expresión coloquial peruana que significa mucho dinero.

—¿Son huaqueros? —pregunta Martín.

—Sí, seguramente son huaqueros.

—El de la trenza estaba en el hotel... —explica Mónica.

—Sí, yo también lo recuerdo —dice Raúl.

Ana también lo recuerda. Tiene miedo, pero no dice nada.

—¿Qué hacemos? —pregunta Martín después de un silencio.

—Tenemos que seguir a esos hombres...

—Si vamos todos, nos verán. Yo iré —dice David—, ustedes esperen aquí.

—Yo voy contigo —dice Laura.

—Y yo... —empieza Mónica, pero Martín las interrumpe.

—David tiene razón. Si vamos todos van a descubrirnos. Él sabrá cómo hablarles si lo ven. Vamos a esperar.

David se mueve entre los árboles y empieza a seguir a los hombres. Los chicos lo miran en silencio. Laura está muy preocupada. Mónica la abraza.

—Sergio estará bien —le dice—. Seguro que David lo encuentra y lo trae.

David sigue a los hombres hasta llegar a la choza. Se esconde detrás de unos árboles. Desde allí ve perfectamente lo que llevan. Se han llevado la cabeza de una estatua pequeña y una fuente entera. «¡Malditos ladrones!», piensa.

Está rojo de rabia. Entonces ve que los hombres abren la puerta de la choza y oye como hablan con alguien. «¡Es Sergio!»

Después oye un golpe y un grito. Quiere ir a ayudar a Sergio, pero se queda quieto, en silencio. Sabe que si va lo cogerán también a él. Los hombres son cuatro. Uno de ellos ha salido fuera de la choza. David ve que lleva un rifle[2]. Decide esperar.

Los hombres guardan las esculturas robadas en la choza. Después se van.

David espera unos minutos, se levanta y avanza hacia la choza. De repente, ve a un hombre de espaldas con un rifle en las manos.

---

2 rifle: arma de fuego larga parecida a un fusil.

«¡Han dejado un vigilante!» David se para. «¿Lo ha visto el hombre?». Lleva el rifle en una mano y fuma una pipa[3] con la otra.

David retrocede en silencio. Luego, muy despacio, vuelve a donde están los chicos.

—¿Qué ha pasado? ¿Has visto a Sergio? —le pregunta Laura, impaciente.

—¿Dónde está Sergio? ¿Lo tienen encerrado? ¿Le han hecho daño? ¿Está bien? —los chicos le preguntan todos a la vez.

—Shhhh —David hace una señal con la mano. —¡Silencio!

Luego escucha. Mira a su alrededor. No se ve a ningún hombre.

—Está encerrado en una choza de piedra cerca de la excavación —explica.

—Pero...

—Sergio está bien, está bien. Lo he oído —David no dice nada del golpe y del grito.

—¿Por qué no ha venido contigo? —pregunta Mónica enfadada.

—Porque no he podido entrar en la choza. Hay un hombre con un rifle en la puerta.

—Y ahora, ¿qué hacemos? —pregunta Raúl.

—Podemos atacarlo[4] por sorpresa —dice Martín, convencido.

David piensa un momento.

—No, es demasiado peligroso. Podría disparar y herir a alguien.

Laura llora en silencio. Sergio y ella salen juntos[5] desde hace tiempo. Mónica la abraza.

Finalmente David dice:

—Creo que lo mejor es separarnos.

—Sí. Estaba pensando lo mismo —dice Mónica—. Unos nos quedamos cerca de la choza por si el hombre se va o se duerme y los otros van a buscar ayuda.

—David, tú debes marcharte. Eres el único que conoce el camino —dice Raúl.

---

3 **pipa**: es un objeto utilizado para fumar tabaco y otras plantas.
4 **atacar**: agredir, asaltar, destrozar.
5 **salir juntos**: tener una relación como pareja pero de manera informal.

—Yo quiero quedarme —dice Laura.

—Yo me quedaré también —dice Martín, que sigue con la idea de atacar por sorpresa al hombre.

—Entonces, nosotros nos vamos —dice David limpiándose las gafas. Se pasa la mano por el pelo desordenado.

—La choza está detrás de las ruinas, hay un camino que lleva allí. Está detrás de unos árboles.

Mónica y Raúl deciden acompañar a David.

—¿Qué haces, Ana? —pregunta David.

—Me quedo con ellos...

—Tengan mucho cuidado —dice David antes de marchar—. Estos hombres son peligrosos.

—Vamos a buscar la choza —dice Martín.

—Pero ¿qué vamos a hacer? —pregunta Laura.

—Vamos a vigilar al hombre del rifle. Quizás se duerme...

Después de caminar un poco, ven a lo lejos la choza. Deciden avanzar escondidos detrás de los árboles. Cuando están cerca, ven al hombre del rifle. Está fumando una pipa.

—Parece pequeño y medio drogado[6]. No puede ser muy fuerte... —murmura Martín mirando al hombre.

—¡Martín, por favor! —Laura contesta también en voz baja— ¿Y si dispara?

De repente oyen gritos y golpes en la puerta de la choza.

—¡Es Sergio! —exclama Ana.

El hombre mira hacia la puerta de la choza. Grita algo y luego ríe.

—¡Sergio, cállate! —dice Laura en voz baja. Teme que el hombre le dispare.

—Si pudiéramos decirle que estamos aquí...

—¿Qué podemos hacer? —pregunta Raúl, pensativo.

De repente, Ana sonríe.

—¡Ya sé! —exclama. Saca de su bolsillo un objeto: ¡la ocarina!

Dentro de la choza, Sergio está nervioso y enfadado. Los hombres han venido, han dejado más esculturas y se han vuelto a marchar.

---

6 drogado: que está bajo los efectos de las drogas.

«¿Piensan dejarlo allí para siempre?» Además, tiene hambre y sed y le duele el golpe que le han dado en el brazo.

Cada vez está más furioso y preocupado. De repente, coge una piedra que está a su lado. No puede distinguir la forma pero es bastante grande. Es una escultura. ¡Todas las piedras son esculturas! La coge con fuerza y golpea la puerta.

Un hombre le grita desde fuera.

—Quieto, huevón⁷ o te pego un tiro —luego ríe.

Sergio calla. Recuerda que uno de los hombres ha cogido un rifle de la choza. ¡Hay un hombre fuera, vigilando con un rifle! Está asustado. No sabe qué hacer.

De repente, oye un sonido. Es un instrumento musical. «Ah, sí, —ahora recuerda—. Es una ocarina, como la de Ana».

«¿Qué hace un hombre con un rifle tocando la ocarina? Seguramente está aburrido», —piensa extrañado—. «Pero se oye muy lejos... ¿Hay más hombres? ¿Está en un campamento de huaqueros...?» Ahora lo ve todo muy negro⁸...

—¿Quién anda acá? —el hombre de fuera grita.

El sonido de la ocarina se para.

Y luego, Sergio oye un disparo. «¿Qué está pasando?»

Sergio cada vez entiende menos.

—¡Ay, Díos mío! —exclama.

Se acurruca en un rincón y se tapa la cabeza con las manos. ¿Le ha llegado el fin⁹?

---

7 **huevón**: insulto que se utiliza en Perú para decir que alguien es tonto.
8 **verlo todo negro**: en sentido figurado, sentirse muy pesimista.
9 **llegar el fin**: estar a punto de morir.

CAPÍTULO 5

David, Mónica y Raúl caminan deprisa. Van en silencio.

Después de un rato, Mónica pregunta:

—David, ¿crees que esos hombres le harán algo a Sergio?

—No lo sé. Creo que no... Ellos saben que está con un grupo de turistas. Saben que sus compañeros avisarán a la policía. No quieren una investigación...

Pero David está preocupado. Sabe que los huaqueros pueden simular un accidente y desviar la atención de los policías.

Finalmente, después de unas horas de camino, llegan a un puesto de la policía en Aguas Calientes.

—Quiero hablar con el Capitán Vargas —dice David al policía que está en la puerta.

Mientras, Jaime, Nuria y Aníbal caminan con el resto del grupo por un sendero estrecho de piedras. Es el final del Camino del Inca. En la puerta del santuario de Machu Picchu hay algunos turistas y estudiantes comprando las entradas para visitar el santuario. Hace calor y la gente va con camisetas y gorros.

—Vamos a ver si David y los chicos ya están aquí —dice Nuria a Jaime, buscando entre la gente.

—Sí, quizás ya han llegado.

—No los veo...

—A lo mejor están dentro.

Aníbal se acerca a ellos.

—Vamos a entrar ahora que aún hay poca gente y puede verse esto mejor —aconseja Aníbal.

—Vale, de acuerdo —dice Jaime.

—¿Nuria? —Guille se acerca a los profesores.

—Sí, Guille, ¿qué pasa?

—Es un poco extraño. ¿Todavía no han llegado los otros?

—No los veo. Quizás ya han entrado.

—Es raro. ¿Por qué no nos han esperado?

—No lo sé. Quizás todavía no han llegado.

—En el bosque, el tiempo no es tan exacto como en las ciudades, chico —interrumpe Aníbal—. No te preocupes, seguro que llegarán enseguida.

Aníbal sonríe, pero Guillermo nota que también está preocupado.

—Bueno. ¿Entramos al Machu Picchu?

Detrás de las montañas de piedra, la ciudad inca se alza magnífica e impresionante. Primero, el grupo va a la Casa del Guardián. Desde allí las vistas son espectaculares.

Varios grupos de turistas caminan entre las ruinas. Guille los mira, pero entre ellos no están sus compañeros.

Después bajan desde la Casa del Guardián hacia el interior de la ciudadela.

—¿Y esto es el sector agrícola¹? —pregunta Jaime señalando unas casas más sencillas con paredes de piedra.

—Sí —explica Aníbal—. Fíjense que la población de Machu Picchu eran gente de la élite social²: agricultores que estudiaban nuevos cultivos, gente de la administración, astrólogos, estudiosos de la naturaleza, sacerdotes, sacerdotisas...

—La parte administrativa es todo eso de allí y la zona religiosa...

En aquel momento se oye un fuerte sonido a lo lejos.

—¿Qué ha sido eso? —pregunta Guille.

—Parecen disparos.

—O truenos...

—No, el cielo está azul.

---

1 **sector agrícola**: es el que se dedica a las actividades agrícolas, es decir a los cultivos de vegetales y hortalizas.

2 **élite social**: es un grupo minoritario dentro de una sociedad y que tiene un estatus superior al resto.

CAPÍTULO 6

Sergio está sentado en un rincón de la choza. Está asustado y preocupado. De repente piensa en la cámara. «¿Dónde está?». La busca a oscuras y la encuentra en el suelo, cerca de él. La coge con fuerza. Piensa que con el *flash* puede sacar fotos de las estatuas robadas. Así se distrae. Y se olvida del miedo.

Entonces vuelve a oír el sonido de la ocarina, pero esta vez el sonido viene de otro lugar. Escucha atentamente. Ahora le parece oír un ruido cerca de la choza. Quizás un animal se está acercando. O un fantasma...

Oye ruido de pasos que se acercan...

¡Y ahora suben por el techo de la choza!

¡Dios mío!, cada vez están más cerca.

—Ahh —Sergio grita asustado.

—Ssshhh —alguien encima de su cabeza le ordena silencio.

—¡No grites! —dice la voz—. Soy yo, Martín.

—¡Martín! Pensaba que eras un fantasma. ¿Dónde están los otros?

—Los otros... ¡Shhh...! Silencio. Alguien llega.

Fuera se oye el ruido de unos pasos que se acercan. Sergio oye como Martín baja rápido del techo de la choza por la parte de fuera.

Los pasos llegan hasta la choza. El hombre del rifle abre la puerta y mira adentro.

—Sí, claro que está aquí —dice. Está muy enfadado—. Pero seguro que hay alguien más por aquí. He oído una ocarina.

Hay otro hombre detrás. Es el hombre de la trenza.

El hombre del rifle mira a su alrededor y dispara al aire dos veces.

—¡Les he visto! —grita— ¡Salgan, malditos!

—¿Qué haces? —grita el hombre de la trenza—. ¿Quieres que nos oigan?

—¡Lo que quiero es agarrar a esos! —el hombre continúa hablando en un idioma que Sergio no entiende. Luego, a través de la puerta abierta, ve que los hombres se pelean. Es que el hombre del rifle quiere disparar otra vez.

—¿Estás loco? —el hombre de la trenza intenta cogerle el rifle. Luchan gritando e insultándose. Caen al suelo.

Sergio se acerca a la puerta de la choza y mira fuera. La luz del sol le hace daño a los ojos. Ve a los dos hombres peleándose y sale en silencio de la choza, con la cámara en la mano. Empieza a caminar deprisa.

De repente, alguien le agarra del brazo.

—¡No grites! —le dice Martín—. Por aquí.

—Martín, ¡qué susto!

—¡Corre!, ¡Corre! Llegan más hombres.

Los chicos salen corriendo y se esconden entre los árboles.

CAPÍTULO 7

—¡Paren ya de pelearse! —el hombre alto llega delante de la choza. Está enfadado.

El hombre de la trenza y el guardián de la choza paran al oír la voz.

Junto al hombre alto hay otros dos huaqueros, que miran divertidos la escena.

—¿Qué pasó...? —pregunta el hombre alto.

—Es que... —empieza el hombre de las trenzas.

—¿Y dónde está el chico? —interrumpe el hombre alto.

—Lo tenemos en la choza... —dice orgulloso el hombre del rifle.

—¿Ah, sí? Interesante, muy interesante —el hombre alto mira la puerta abierta de la choza...

—¿Estás bien? —Laura abraza a su amigo.

—¡Laura! —exclama Sergio, contento de verla de nuevo.

Ana los está esperando. Tiene su ocarina en la mano.

—¡Sergio! ¿Nos has oído? —pregunta la chica.

—¡La ocarina! —exclama Sergio. —¡Ahora lo entiendo!

—Vamos, no podemos perder tiempo —dice Martín que ha visto acercarse a la choza a los tres huaqueros.

Sergio y sus compañeros empiezan a correr hasta llegar al camino. Finalmente se paran para descansar un poco.

—Sigamos caminando —dice Martín.

—¿Dónde están los otros? —pregunta Sergio.

—Han ido a Aguas Calientes a buscar a la policía. Vamos, seguro que los huaqueros van a perseguirnos.

—¿Sabéis el camino a Aguas Calientes?

—Los encontraremos en Machu Picchu. Está muy cerca de aquí. Los del grupo ya deben estar allí hace horas.

—Sí, vamos.

Los chicos siguen por el camino. El día es claro. El sol calienta a estas horas del día.

—¡Esperad! —Laura se para de repente— ¿No habéis oído?

—¿Qué has oído?

—No sé. Creo que he oído un disparo...

—¿Un disparo? ¿Crees que nos siguen?

—No. Ha sonado lejos.

—Será algún animal.

—Sí, claro. Seguramente.

—Tal vez los huaqueros se están matando entre ellos.

—Vamos rápido. Quiero llegar a Machu Picchu —dice Ana caminando deprisa.

Continúan en silencio por el camino. Llevan mucho rato andando deprisa y están cansados.

—Debemos estar muy cerca de Machu Picchu... —dice Ana que está nerviosa. Todos están nerviosos.

—Sí, seguro...

—¿No es aquello Machu Picchu? —dice Martín señalando a lo lejos los muros de la ciudad sagrada.

—Sí, creo que sí.

—¡Menos mal! —exclama Sergio— ¡Tengo un hambre! —ahora Sergio está más tranquilo.

—Sergio, ¿has sacado fotos? —pregunta Laura.

—Sí, muchas. De las ruinas y de lo que han robado. Están aquí, en la cámara —dice y ríe contento.

De repente, Laura se para a escuchar.

—¿Qué pasa ahora? —pregunta Ana, que está asustada.

—No sé. Creo que nos siguen...

—Laura, ¡estás paranoica¹! Estamos en el bosque y hay un montón de animales por aquí que hacen ruido —dice Martín.

---

1 **estar paranoica**: en lenguaje coloquial, imaginar peligros inexistentes; en referencia a la enfermedad psiquiátrica en la que se tienen delirios e ideas persecutorias obsesivas.

—O quizá hay otro grupo por aquí... —dice Sergio.

—Sí, tienes razón —sonríe Laura —vamos, deprisa. Tengo ganas de llegar.

—Ese chico ha pasado por aquí. Estoy seguro. Y no está solo.

—¡Vamos, deprisa! —los tenemos que atrapar antes de llegar a la ciudad. El hombre del pelo negro y trenzas camina deprisa. El huaquero del rifle lo sigue.

—¡Cómo se ha enfadado el jefe, ¿eh? —dice.

—Sí, si no encontramos al chico, nos mata...

CAPÍTULO 8

—Mira, ¡allá están...!

—Sí, son ellos...

—Damos la vuelta por este cerro[1] —dice el huaquero del rifle— y entonces...

—Sí, entonces, ¡pum, pum!

—Sí, ¡ja, ja, ja...! —los huaqueros ríen.

—Anda nomás, por aquí, sin hacer ruido...

Los huaqueros salen del camino. Empiezan a correr por el cerro.

Poco después llegan de nuevo al camino. Se esconden y esperan a los chicos.

—Hey, compadre. Por allá llegan ahorita...

—Apunta bien, «Pelao».

—Ahora apunto nomás. Yo no fallo... ¡je, je, je...!

Los chicos se acercan al lugar donde están los huaqueros. Sergio y Laura van delante. Detrás le sigue Ana y después Martín, que está mirando el paisaje a su alrededor.

Sergio le está explicando a Laura otra vez su aventura con los huaqueros:

—... y entonces me encerraron en la choza. Dentro estaba todo oscuro...

Ahora los huaqueros están a pocos metros de los chicos.

—Ahora, «Pelao». Empieza por el de los anteojos[2]...

—Sí, compadre. A por ese voy.

El huaquero apunta.

—Ya es mío —el hombre dispara pero no pasa nada.

---

1 **cerro:** elevación del terreno de menor altura que una montaña.

2 **anteojos:** gafas en algunas zonas de América.

— ¡¡¡Pum!!! —dice el hombre del pelo negro y las trenzas, riendo. Su diente de oro brilla por un momento.

Los chicos continúan caminando. El hombre del rifle dispara otra vez. No se oye ningún disparo.

—¿Qué fue, «Pelao»?

—No tenemos balas, nomás.

—¿No tenemos balas?

—No, no tenemos balas, compadre.

El hombre de las trenzas negras no se lo puede creer. Los dos hombres se miran.

—No hay balas... —repite.

—No, ni una bala...

—Pues sin balas...

—Y ahora, ¿qué hacemos? —pregunta «Pelao»— ¡El jefe nos va a matar!

—Yo sé qué hacer —dice su compañero sacando una navaja de su bolsillo. Ríe. Su risa es muy desagradable.

Los dos hombres se acercan por detrás a los chicos. El hombre del rifle también ha sacado una navaja y la abre.

Los chicos caminan delante de ellos, hablando.

Los hombres ahora están muy cerca. Caminan sin hacer ruido.

Los chicos están cansados, pero van rápido. Tienen prisa por llegar a Machu Picchu.

—Tú vas al chico y la chica de la izquierda —dice el hombre del rifle—. Y yo voy a por los otros. Al de los anteojos lo quiero yo.

—¡Está bien, «Pelao»! ¿Estás preparado?

—Sí. ¡Vamos!

—*Please, please*! —de repente se oyen unas voces a sus espaldas— *Oh, sorry!*[3]

3 *Oh, sorry!:* ¡Oh perdón!

Los dos hombres esconden sus navajas. Un grupo de turistas americanos se acerca a ellos. Visten con pantalones cortos, sandalias y llevan cámaras de fotos.

—¿De dónde han salido estos? —pregunta «Pelao» sorprendido.

—*Can you take a picture for us?* [4] —y dice más despacio— «¿Puede tomar foto de nosotros con ustedes?»

—Nosotros *no English. No English...* —dice el huaquero de las trenzas sonriendo y enseñando su diente de oro.

—¡Oh...! —dice una señora gorda y simpática sonriendo. —*Foto Machu Picchu, you, local, and us.*

—Quieren una foto... —le explica el hombre de las trenzas a su compañero.

—¡Maldita sea! —exclama este, hablando entre dientes.

—*That is Machu Picchu, isn't it?* [5] —pregunta un hombre de aspecto amable—*Come here! A picture... foto, ustedes, us and Machu Picchu in the background* [6].

A lo lejos se puede ver ya claramente la ciudad de Machu Picchu. Hay grupos de turistas en la entrada. Hay un poco de cola para comprar los *tickets*.

—¡Ya hemos llegado! —exclama Laura, contenta— ¡Ya estamos en Machu Picchu!

—Vamos, corred, seguramente el grupo ya estará dentro...

—¿Creéis que David, Mónica y Raúl ya han avisado a la policía?

—*Yes*, sí..., foto, sí, sí, anden aquí nomás... sí, sí... aquí. Ponte allá, tú con los gringos... Eso, nosotros en el centro, los gringos al lado, sí, pase delante, que se vea... y Machu Picchu detrás... así, una sonrisa...

Los dos hombres hablan entre ellos en voz baja.

4 *Can you take a picture of us?:* ¿Puede tomarnos una foto?
5 *That is Machu Picchu, isn't it?:* Esto es Machu Pichu, ¿no?
6 *Come here! A picture... us and Machu Picchu in the backround:* Venid hacia aquí! Una foto, con ustedes, nosotros y Machu Picchu de fondo.

—Esos chicos malditos seguro que ya han entrado a Machu Picchu.

—No pasa nada, nosotros también vamos a entrar... No se nos escaparán.

—No podemos hacer nada con esos gringos aquí. ¿Cuánto tiempo hace que no has visitado Machu Picchu?

—No lo he visto nunca. Yo soy de la costa.

El hombre de las trenzas acaricia su navaja. ¡Su mirada es terrible!

—No los veo —dice Laura mirando a su alrededor.

Laura y sus amigos han entrado ya a Machu Picchu. Miran atentos a su alrededor. Buscan a sus compañeros del instituto.

—Es que esto es muy grande...

—Quizás no han llegado, todavía.

—Seguro que sí. Ya es muy tarde.

—Vamos buscando. Ya los encontraremos.

Están en una explanada. Hay algunos turistas paseando y tomando fotos. De repente, Laura ve a un chico un poco gordo y pelirrojo comiendo un bocadillo. Está de espaldas a ellos.

—¡Guille! —grita contenta.

—*Entschuldigung*?[7] —exclama una señora mayor, volviéndose y mirando a Laura.

—¡Oh! Perdone, señora, me he confundido.

—¿Quién es? —le preguntan Martín y Ana a Laura.

—Me he equivocado. He confundido a esa señora alemana con Guille...

—¡Ja, ja, ja...! —Martín y Ana ríen. Ahora, en Machu Picchu se sienten seguros. Están contentos e impacientes por encontrar a sus compañeros. Quieren explicarles todas las aventuras que han vivido.

—¿Los habéis visto? —pregunta Martín, acercándose.

—No, todavía no.

—Aquí hay mucha gente —dice Sergio—. Subamos arriba, será más fácil verlos.

---

7 *Entschuldigung!:* Disculpe, en alemán.

—¡Aquí están...! —dice el huaquero de las trenzas.

—Hay mucha gente ahí...

—Sí, «Pelao». Tenemos que esperar...

—Vamos a seguirlos de lejos..

—¡Allá! —dice Martín. —¡Son ellos!

—¿Tú crees?

Han subido a lo alto de una terraza para tener una visión más amplia. Están solos, mirando a los turistas que se ven pequeños abajo.

—Sí, ¿no es Jaime aquel...? —pregunta Ana.

—No sé, están lejos.

—Sí, es Jaime —dice Sergio. —Y aquel, allá abajo, es Aníbal.

—¡Y Guille y Nuria!...

—¡Eh!, ¡eh! —los chicos gritan y mueven los brazos.

—No nos oyen. Están demasiado lejos...

—Aquí los tenemos —los huaqueros están unos metros detrás de los chicos.

—En esta parte no hay gente.

—¡Agarrémoslos! —dice «el Pelao», que ahora no lleva el rifle.

—Sí, el de los anteojos es para ti.

Los hombres avanzan silenciosamente. Ahora están a pocos metros de los chicos. Estos se han acercado a un balcón[8] para ver mejor a sus compañeros y poder avisarles. A sus pies está el vacío[9].

—Guarda la navaja, «Pelao». Un empujón y «adiós». Un triste accidente.

—¡Je, je! Sí, un triste accidente: cuatro chicos se caen y se matan en un triste accidente en Machu Picchu.

—¡Genial!

---

8 **balcón**: es una especie de plataforma que se proyecta desde la pared de un edificio. En las construcciones actuales tienen normalmente una barandilla. En este caso, en las ruinas, da directamente al vacío.

9 **vacío**: cualquier lugar muy profundo en el que hay una gran distancia hasta llegar al fondo.

—¡Hay que agarrarlos!, ¡Corramos! —gritan los huaqueros empezando a correr hacia los chicos.

—¡Eh!, ¡Laura, Sergio! Por fin os encontramos.

Los chicos se vuelven y ven a Mónica, Raúl y David que se acercan, seguidos de dos policías.

—¡Mónica! —los chicos se vuelven y empiezan a correr hacia ellos, contentos.

—Pero...¿qué hacen estos? —exclama un policía. —¡Están locos!

Dos hombres están corriendo hacia el borde del balcón, de donde se acaban de apartar Laura y sus amigos y saltan al vacío.

—¡Aaaah..... ! —gritan. —«Pelao», ¡Dios mío!

—Compadre.. ¡¡¡Aaahhh!!!

—Pero ¿qué hacen estos hombres? —pregunta Mónica al verlos saltar —¿representan una ceremonia inca?

—No, son los huaqueros —dice David, que no puede creer lo que ve.

A lo lejos se oyen unas voces que los llaman:

—¡Laura, Martín...!

—¡Eh, Mónica, Sergio, Raúl...!

Guille y sus compañeros, y Jaime y Nuria los han visto y se acercan. Están contentos de verlos de nuevo.

Cuando llegan donde están, se abrazan.

—¿Habéis visto unos hombres que han saltado por las terrazas? —pregunta Guille— ¿Es un ritual o un espectáculo para turistas?

—No, no —dice David—. Es una historia un poco larga de explicar. Les presento al capitán Vargas y a un colega de la policía.

—Capitán Vargas, ellos son Nuria y Jaime, los profesores, y estos chicos son Sergio y sus amigos. Y estos, los compañeros de la escuela.

—Mucho gusto.

—Ahora vamos a sentarnos y hablar un poco —dice el capitán Vargas—. Estos chicos han vivido una aventura muy peligrosa...

—¿Qué ha pasado? —pregunta Guille— ¡Ya decía yo que llegabais muy tarde...!

—Ahora tengo que llevarme a Sergio y a sus amigos al cuartel para que nos expliquen todo lo que han pasado—el capitán Vargas organiza sus investigaciones.

Luego se acerca al balcón.

—¡Ay, compadre... qué dolor!

—«Pelao», me he roto un hueso...

—Sánchez, avise al cuartel que vengan por estos dos —ordena el capitán Vargas—. Vigílenlos, parece que solo están heridos. También tengo que hablar con ellos...

—Chicos, vamos a ir todos a Aguas Calientes a hablar de este viaje tan especial...

—¿Irnos ahora sin visitar Machu Picchu? —Mónica parece aterrorizada— ¿Sin visitar la ciudad sagrada? ¡Ni hablar!

—Yo los llevo a la comisaría en un ratito— dice David sonriendo al capitán—. Los chicos merecen un poco de diversión ahora.

David coge de la mano a Mónica.

—Ahora voy a llevarte a un sitio que te va a encantar, subimos estas escaleras y desde arriba verás el templo del Sol, las fuentes y el Intihuatana[10].

—¡¡¡No vamos a subir otra vez!!! —se queja Guille.

—Guille —Laura le coge del brazo—, creo que la invitación no es para todos... Vamos con el grupo, anda.

Mónica y David se alejan de la mano y David grita a los demás:

—Nos vemos luego en la entrada. ¡No se alejen!

---

10 **Intihuatana:** es el centro de cada construcción religiosa del imperio inca.

DESPUÉS DE LA LECTURA

CAPÍTULOS 1, 2 Y 3

1. ¿Qué es?

Relaciona los siguientes nombres con sus definiciones correspondientes y forma frases.

Ejemplo: *Wiñaywayna son unas ruinas arqueológicas que se encuentran en el camino del Inca.*

> Urubamba - huaqueros - porteadores - San Blas
>
> Machu Picchu - Inca - Wiñaywayna - Cusco

Ruinas arqueológicas en el camino del Inca.
Ladrones de objetos arqueológicos.
Pueblo, montaña, provincia y río en Perú.
Ciudad de Perú.
Antiguo poblado inca.
Barrio de Cusco.
Civilización andina que creó un importante imperio en el siglo XII.
Personas que llevan las mochilas de los turistas o excursionistas.

2. ¿Cómo? ¿Dónde? ¿Por qué? ¿Qué?

A. Responde con tus propias palabras.

a. ¿De qué ciudad sale el grupo para ir a Machu Picchu?
b. ¿Quién va en el grupo además de los chicos de la clase?
c. ¿Cómo realizan la excursión? A pie, en tren, en autobús, en bicicleta... Descríbelo.
d. ¿Porqué se marean los chicos en la excursión?
e. ¿Qué época del año es?
f. ¿Por qué Mónica quiere visitar las ruinas de Brutthalva?
g. ¿Qué es una ocarina?
h. ¿Qué condición pone David para visitar las ruinas de Brutthalva?
i. ¿Por qué le dice Laura a Mónica que con David podrían vivir en una biblioteca?

B. Termina las frases.

a. El plan de los chicos para estos días es ....
b. Hace calor, pero Nuria les aconseja ....
c. El hombre del diente de oro dice que no es buena idea visitar las ruinas de Brutthalva porque ....
d. David no cree que las voces que oyen sean de turistas porque...
e. Los huaqueros se llevan el material de las ruinas para ....
f. Sergio quiere volver a las ruinas para ....

3. ¿Cuál?

En estas palabras relacionadas con Perú hay un intruso, ¿cuál?

Cusco • Andes • Inca • ruinas • Urubamba • Bogotá

4. ¿Quién es quién?

A. Describe físicamente a los personajes con tus propias palabras.

B. Según sus aficiones, ¿a quién corresponde cada descripción?

a. Le gusta mucho la historia de los Incas.
b. No le gusta caminar y le gusta comer.
c. Le gusta caminar por las montañas.
d. Le gusta Mónica.
e. Le gusta hacer fotos.

5. Y ahora tú...

A. De las aficiones de los personajes, di las que te gustan a ti o si te gustan otras.

B. ¿Has hecho algún viaje de final de curso? ¿Dónde?

C. ¿Has visitado algunas ruinas? ¿Cuáles? ¿Qué te han parecido?

D. ¿Te gustaría realizar un *trekking* con tus amigos? ¿Por qué?

E. Describe a tu personaje favorito de la historia.

6. ¿Cuál es?

Escoge el final de frase correcto.

1. Los huaqueros esperan...
a. ... comer pasta para cenar.
b. ... que les den mucho dinero por lo robado.
c. ... construir una choza con los materiales robados.

2. David no entra en la choza a rescatar a Sergio porque...
a. ... hay un hombre fuera con un rifle.
b. ... se queda paralizado de miedo.
c. ... prefiere que entren todos juntos a rescatarlo.

3. David marcha con algunos chicos a Aguas Calientes...
a. ... para pedir ayuda.
b. ... para reunirse con le resto de grupo.
c. ... porque es muy tarde y no quiere perder más tiempo.

4. Ana toca la ocarina para...
a. ... burlarse del guardián de la choza.
b. ... avisar a Sergio de que están allí.
c. ... pasar el rato.

5. Los huaqueros se pelean entre ellos porque...
a. ... uno dispara el rifle.
b. ... todos quieren quedarse las esculturas.
c. ... unos quieren liberar a Sergio y otros no.

7. ¿Qué hacen?

Completa las siguientes frases con el verbo correspondiente en presente.

> seguir, esconderse, ser, estar, llegar, abrir, encerrar

a. Los hombres .... a Sergio en una choza.
b. David .... a los hombres hasta llegar a la choza.
c. Finalmente David y algunos chicos .... a Aguas Calientes.
d. Desde la Casa de la Guardia las vistas .... espectaculares.
e. Sergio .... sentado en la choza.
f. El hombre del rifle .... la puerta y mira dentro de la choza.
g. Los chicos salen corriendo y .... entre los árboles.

8. ¿Dónde están?

En este punto de la historia, los personajes están distribuidos en varios grupos. Clasifícalos según su localización.

> en la cabaña

> cerca de la cabaña

> en el camino de Aguas Calientes

> en el Machu Picchu

9. ¿Es verdad?

Marca si es verdadero o falso.

a. Sergio vuelve a las ruinas porque se ha olvidado de sacar fotos. V F
b. Sergio se escapa de los huaqueros y se esconde en una choza. V F
c. Mónica y Sergio salen juntos desde hace algún tiempo. V F
d. Martín no quiere acercarse a la choza porque está muy asustado. V F
e. El hombre que vigila la choza lleva un rifle y toca la ocarina. V F
f. David va a Aguas Calientes a buscar ayuda. V F

10. ¿Castellano de España o del Perú?

Algunas palabras que utiliza la gente de Perú son distintas de las que se usan en España. Anota algunas palabras o expresiones que pienses que se dicen de forma diferente.

11. Y ahora tú...

Con estos verbos haz tus propias frases relacionadas con la historia.

vigilar ▪ disparar ▪ fumar ▪ tocar

CAPÍTULOS 7 Y 8

12. ¿Qué pasa? ¿Cómo?

Describe con tus propias palabras las siguientes escenas.

a. Sergio escapa de la choza.
b. Sergio, Martín, Laura y Ana están nerviosos mientras van a Machu Picchu.
c. Los huaqueros persiguen a los chicos.
d. Unos turistas se cruzan en el camino.
e. Los huaqueros cambian de planes.

13. ¿Qué falta?

Completa las frases con el enlace correcto.

> para, pero, por, sin, pero, con,

a. Los chicos oyen ruidos .... piensan que son animales.
b. Los hombres disparan .... no tienen balas.
c. Los chicos tienen prisa .... llegar a Machu Picchu.
d. Laura confunde a Guille .... una turista alemana.
e. En la entrada de Machu Picchu hay un poco de cola .... comprar los *tickets*.
f. Mónica no quiere irse de Machu Picchu .... visitarla.

14. ¿Cuál?

Relaciona un elemento de cada grupo y forma tres frases con sentido en esta historia.

Los huaqueros	perseguir	Machu Picchu
Guille	preocuparse	amigos
Los turistas	sacar fotos	chicos

15. ¿Qué dicen y qué quieren decir?

Escoge la opción correcta.

A. Cuando uno de los huaqueros dice «Al de las gafas lo quiero yo», quiere decir que:

a. Él tiene mucho cariño a Sergio.
b. Él quiere atacar personalmente a Sergio.
c. Quiere tener unas gafas.

B. Cuando Anibal dice «el tiempo en el bosque no es tan exacto como en las ciudades», quiere decir que:

a. No hace buen tiempo en el bosque.
b. En el bosque no se calcula el tiempo con tanta exactitud como en las ciudades.
c. En el bosque no se sabe nunca qué hora es.

16. Después de leer...

Encuentra en esta sopa de letras seis palabras relacionadas con la cultura de Perú.

B	H	A	T	K	C	B	A	T	A	D	C	R	E	P
C	H	V	A	N	Q	U	L	J	D	F	O	X	C	B
H	U	T	P	Q	U	E	C	H	U	A	L	R	U	G
A	A	G	A	F	A	I	C	B	A	R	L	M	Z	E
Q	Q	B	U	R	U	B	A	M	B	A	A	L	C	A
U	U	C	T	S	X	C	B	E	A	B	I	W	O	Z
E	E	D	A	B	R	A	K	R	F	S	N	K	L	Ñ
T	R	U	I	N	A	S	R	S	H	I	C	N	E	E
A	O	T	Q	U	E	C	H	U	A	V	A	N	Y	P
L	S	L	N	F	A	S	C	Y	K	C	S	A	T	Y

17. ¿Cuándo?

Ordena las frases tal como suceden en este capítulo.

☐ **a.** La policía coge a los huaqueros.
☐ **b.** En el kilómetro 82 empiezan el *trekking*.
☐ **c.** Los huaqueros siguen a los chicos por el camino a Machu Picchu.
☐ **d.** Llegan a Machu Picchu.
☐ **e.** Los chicos están en un hostal en Cusco.
☐ **f.** David con algunos chicos va a buscar ayuda a Aguas Calientes.
☐ **g.** Sergio se escapa.
☐ **h.** David sale temprano con algunos chicos para visitar Brutthalva.
☐ **i.** Unos turistas americanos les piden para hacer fotos.
☐ **j.** Visitan Wiñaywayna.
☐ **k.** Los huaqueros encierran a Sergio en una choza.

18. Y ahora tú...

A. Pon un título a cada capítulo que explica lo más importante que pasa en él.

B. Piensa otros peligros que podrían pasar en un *trekking* de estas características.

C. ¿Te interesa la historia de los incas? ¿Y de otras civilizaciones antiguas? ¿Por qué?

SOLUCIONES

1 Wiñaywayna son unas ruinas arqueológicas que se encuentran en el camino del Inca.

Los huaqueros son ladrones de objetos arqueológicos.

Urubamba es el nombre de un pueblo y también de una montaña, de una provincia y de un río.

Cusco es una ciudad de Perú.

Machu Picchu es una antiguo poblado inca.

San Blas es un barrio de Cusco.

Los Incas fueron una civilización andina que creó un importante imperio en el siglo XII.

Los porteadores son las personas que llevan las mochilas de los turistas o excursionistas.

2 A

a. El grupo sale de Cusco.

b. Los profesores, los guías y los porteadores.

c. El grupo sale de Cusco y va en autobús hasta el km 84 desde donde empiezan a caminar.

d. Por la altura.

e. Verano, época seca.

f. Porque todavía no las han abierto al público.

g. La ocarina es un pequeño instrumento musical de viento.

h. Que los profesores tienen que estar de acuerdo.

i. Es una broma que se refiere al gusto de los dos por la historia.

B

a. El plan de los chicos para estos días es hacer un *trekking* de dos días hasta Machu Picchu y después visitar Cusco y sus alrededores.

b. Hace calor, pero Nuria les aconseja llevar algo de abrigo.

c. El hombre del diente de oro dice que no es buena idea visitar las ruinas de Brutthalva porque están lejos del camino, no son interesantes y están en una zona maldita.

d. David no cree que las voces que oyen sean de turistas porque están fuera de ruta.

e. Los huaqueros se llevan el material de las ruinas para venderlo.

f. Sergio quiere volver a las ruinas para sacar fotos.

3 Bogotá.

4 A

Nuria es la tutora de la clase. Es una mujer simpática, de pelo largo y castaño.

David es el guía. Es bajo, moreno, delgado y lleva gafas redondas.

Martín es un chico delgado, atlético y con el pelo castaño y rizado.

B a. Mónica; **b.** Guille; **c.** Martín; **d.** David; **e.** Sergio.

6 1 **b**; 2 **a**; 3 **a**; 4 **b**; 5 **a**

7

a. Los hombres **encierran** a Sergio en una choza.

b. David **sigue** a los hombres hasta llegar a la choza.

c. Finalmente David y algunos chicos **llegan** a Aguas Calientes.

d. Desde la Casa de la Guardia las vistas **son** espectaculares.

e. Sergio **está sentado** en la choza.

f. El hombre del rifle abre la puerta y **mira** dentro de la choza.

g. Los chicos salen corriendo y **se esconden** entre los árboles.

8

En la cabaña: Sergio.

Cerca de la cabaña: Ana, Laura, Martín.

En el camino de Aguas Calientes: David, Raúl, Mónica.

En el Machu Picchu: resto del grupo, profesores, Aníbal y porteadores.

9 a. V; **b.** F; **c.** F; **d.** F; **e.** F; **d.** V

10 Agarrar, ahorita, huaqueros, huevón, nomás, ómnibus, *snack*.

11 Posible respuesta:
El hombre del rifle vigila la choza.
El huaquero dispara al aire dos veces.
El vigilante fuma una pipa.
Ana toca la ocarina para avisar a Sergio de su presencia.

12 Posible respuesta:
a. Sergio al ver la puerta abierta sale de la choza. Se encuentra con Martín y los dos se van corriendo.
b. Sergio, Martín, Laura y Ana en el camino hacia Machu Picchu oyen ruidos y piensan que pueden seguirles. Caminan deprisa y tienen ganas de llegar.
c. Los huaqueros van detrás de los chicos y esperan una oportunidad para atacarlos.
d. Los huaqueros se encuentran en el camino con unos turistas americanos que quieren hacerse unas fotos con ellos.
e. Como los americanos han entretenido a los hombres y estos ven que no alcanzarán a los chicos deciden seguirles hasta el interior de Machu Picchu y atacarlos allá.

13 a. Los chicos oyen ruidos **y/pero** piensan que son animales.
b. Los hombres disparan **pero** no tienen balas.
c. Los chicos tienen prisa **por** llegar a Machu Picchu.
d. Laura confunde a Guille **con** una turista alemana.
e. En la entrada de Machu Picchu hay un poco de cola **para** comprar los *tickets*.
f. Mónica no quiere irse de Machu Picchu **sin** visitarla.

14 Posible respuesta:

Los huaqueros persiguen a los chicos.

Guille se preocupa por sus amigos.

Los turistas quieren hacerse una foto delante de Machu Picchu.

15 A a; **B** b

16

B	H	A	T	K	C	B	A	T	A	D	C	R	E	P
C	H	V	A	N	Q	U	L	J	D	F	O	X	C	B
H	U	T	P	Q	U	E	C	H	U	A	L	R	U	G
A	A	G	A	F	A	I	C	B	A	R	L	M	S	E
Q	Q	B	U	R	U	B	A	M	B	A	A	L	C	A
U	U	C	T	S	X	C	B	E	A	B	I	W	O	Z
E	E	D	A	B	R	A	K	R	F	S	N	K	L	Ñ
T	R	U	I	N	A	S	R	S	H	I	C	N	E	E
A	O	T	Q	U	E	C	H	U	A	V	A	N	Y	P
L	S	L	N	F	A	S	C	Y	K	C	S	A	T	Y

17 1 **e**; 2 **b**; 3 **j**; 4 **h**; 5 **k**; 6 **f**; 7 **g**; 8 **c**; 9 **i**; 10 **d**; 11 **a**.

The Autumn Princess

Nick and Claire Page

Illustrations by Beverley Young

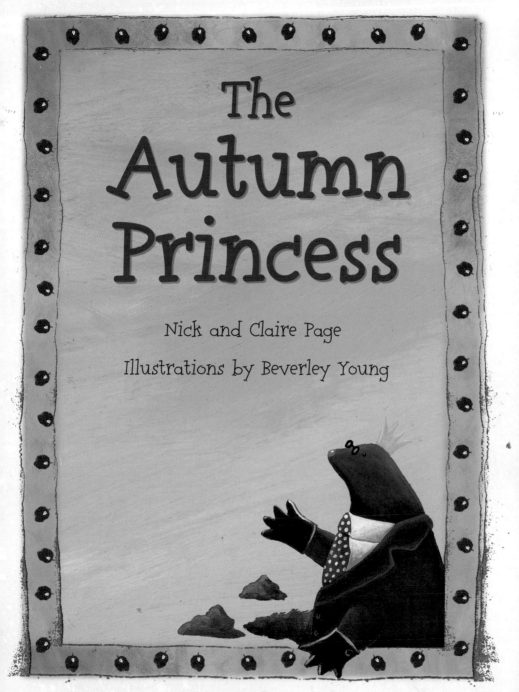

make
believe
ideas

The Autumn Princess had plum-red hair and eyes the color of emeralds. She helped her parents, the King and Queen of Autumn, to look after everything in the Old Orchard.

She loved talking to the apple trees in
the orchard. They had names like Bess Pool,
Black Jack, Annie Elizabeth, Crimson Costard,
Cornish Gillyflower and Gipsy King.

Her favorite was Golden Pippin. He let
her climb his branches and gave her
delicious fruit. When the wind blew, he
would rock her to sleep. The other trees
could talk, but Golden Pippin was silent
and a little sad.

One day, the king and queen said, "It is time for us to look after another orchard. You must take over here. We shall find someone to look after you and help you."

The king said, "You need someone down-to-earth, to keep you safe from harm."

The queen said, "No, you need someone to lift you up, to show you new adventures."

So Old Oak, the wisest and oldest tree in the orchard, announced a contest: "Whoever loves the princess the most shall marry her!"

Immediately, the Prince of the Earth
burst from underground! He was dressed
in a blue-black suit of softest velvet.
"Autumn Princess," he said, "I have loved
you from the depths of the earth. We
will be happy and safe underground."

"Super!" said the king. "That's settled then."
But the Autumn Princess said,
"I can't live under the ground. I need the orchard and the orchard needs me. But thank you for your offer."

Then the Prince of the Air came down
from the sky! He was dressed in a
blue-black coat of finest feathers.
"Autumn Princess," he said, "I have
loved you from the heights of the sky.
We will be happy and free in the clouds."

"Super!" said the queen. "That decides it."
But the Autumn Princess said, "I can't
live up in the sky. I need the orchard
and the orchard needs me. But thank
you for applying."

"The Prince of the Earth has won!" said the king.
"The Prince of the Air has won!" said the queen.
"But I don't want either of them!" said the Autumn Princess.
And she burst into tears and ran off.

She sat at the foot of Golden Pippin and wept. The tree drank in her tears as they fell. He showered her with a blanket of leaves and dropped two apples, like tears, for her to eat.

Old Oak saw this and said, "I know who truly loves the Autumn Princess. He is rooted in the ground, but he reaches into the sky. He can keep her safe and allow her to climb."

"**Super**," said the king and the queen. "**Who?**"
"Golden Pippin," said Old Oak.
"**She can't marry a tree!**" said the king.
"You'll have to trust me on this one,"
replied Old Oak.

19

They said to the princess, **"We know who loves you the most."**

"Who?" she asked.

"Golden Pippin," they said.

The princess burst into tears, but this time because she was so happy.

They said to Golden Pippin, "Will you look after the Autumn Princess?"

"He can't speak," said the princess. "Just wave your branches, then," said the king.

But from deep inside the tree came the words: "I will."

There was a huge crack! Like a seed breaking open, or a cloud parting to show the sun, the tree opened and out came a handsome prince.

"The enchantment is broken!" boomed Old Oak. He told how, long ago, a prince had tried to chop down the orchard. So the magic of the woods had turned him into a tree, until he could learn to love the orchard.

Golden Pippin and the Autumn Princess
were married at Apple Harvest. For the rest
of their life together, they looked after the
orchard as no one else ever had or ever will.

25

Ready to tell

Oh no! Some of the pictures from this story have been mixed up! Can you retell the story and point to each picture in the correct order?

26

Picture dictionary

Encourage your child to read these harder words from the story and gradually develop their basic vocabulary.

autumn

crack

handsome

harvest

king

orchard

prince

princess

queen

Key words

Here are some key words used in context. Help your child to use other words from the border in simple sentences.

She is **going** away.

Old Oak **was** wise.

Who loves **the** princess?

This tree loves her.

He and **she** are happy.

Host an apple-tasting!

There are many different types of apples. Some traditional varieties have interesting names and may be quite rare.

You will need

5 or 6 eating apples of different types. (It's usually easy to buy Golden Delicious or Macintosh apples, but can you find less common ones like a Russet or Pippin?) • paper plates (one for each apple) • crayons • green paper • scissors • sticky tape • paper to write on

What to do

1 Color the paper plates to look like the apples. Cut leaf shapes from the green paper and tape them to the plate.
2 Write a numbered list with the name of each apple.
3 Copy each number onto a different paper plate.
4 With a grown-up's help, cut each apple into chunks. Put the pieces on the plate with the matching number.
5 Give each person a piece of paper and a pen or pencil. Ask them to taste each apple and write down what they think about it. For example, do they like its flavor? Is it crunchy or not? Is it sweet or sharp?
6 When everyone has tasted all the apples, get each person to choose his or her favorite.

Now you can tell everyone the name of each apple and enjoy eating them. You could serve apple juice, too.

FIVE METAPHYSICAL POETS

FIVE METAPHYSICAL POETS

DONNE

HERBERT   VAUGHAN

CRASHAW   MARVELL

by

JOAN BENNETT, M.A.

Fellow of Girton College, Cambridge

CAMBRIDGE
AT THE UNIVERSITY PRESS
1971

PUBLISHED BY

THE SYNDICS OF THE CAMBRIDGE UNIVERSITY PRESS

Bentley House, 200 Euston Road, London, NW1 2DB
American Branch: 32 East 57th Street, New York, N.Y. 10022

THIS EDITION

© CAMBRIDGE UNIVERSITY PRESS 1964

ISBN

0 521 04156 2 clothbound
0 521 09238 8 paperback

First issued as *Four Metaphysical Poets*
First edition 1934
Second edition 1953
Reprinted with corrections 1957
This edition, with a new chapter on
Marvell 1964
Reprinted 1966
Reprinted 1971

First printed in Great Britain at the University Press, Cambridge
Reprinted by offset-lithography by John Dickens & Co., Ltd.
Northampton

PREFACE TO
THE SECOND EDITION

I HAVE revised but not substantially altered this introduction to four seventeenth century poets. In some
ways my approach to these poets may be said to
belong to the nineteen-thirties. There is an underlying
assumption that the reader will be familiar with and responsive to nineteenth century romantic poetry, and
that the prosaic images, the rhythms of speech and the
logical complexity of metaphysical poetry may at first repel
him. Today the reader is more accustomed to difficult
poetry; he no longer expects tunefulness or images that
delight the senses. The qualities of lucidity and logical
coherence in metaphysical poetry are more likely to seem
strange to him now than the rarity of evocative rhythms
and sense-delighting figures. Perhaps, today, that lucidity
needs to be stressed and even excused. Modern critics often
encourage us to look in poetry for fragments of meaning
not wholly intended by the poet nor within his control.
But the metaphysical poet knew what he meant; though
rhythm and imagery enhance his meaning, they do not
make it ambiguous. The only ambiguity that the reader
should look for is the intentional pun, anagram or emblem. If I were beginning again today, I should find
myself trying to show how, nevertheless, the best in this
kind are poems and not merely witty verses. The meaning
is unambiguous, but more disturbing and far-reaching than
the most exact prose paraphrase. It is not only conveyed to
the reason but 'proved on the pulses' by the poet's rhythm
and diction. These poets were skilled and subtle masters of
metre, and they had something to say that required the
language of poetry.

But I have not rewritten this book; I have sometimes

modified a statement that now seems rash, I have expanded
or rewritten sentences that now seem to me misleading or
obscure, I have often expanded the quotations, giving,
wherever possible, the whole poem rather than a fragment.
I have also added interpretations of some stanzas which I
now know (through the experience of teaching) are more
difficult than I then recognized. Finally I have revised the
text of the poems quoted to accord with the editions cited
in the bibliographical note.

JOAN BENNETT

September 1952

A Note on the date of Donne's birth.

In previous impressions of this book I have given 1573
as the date of Donne's birth. I take this opportunity of
changing this on the evidence in Professor F. P. Wilson's
article entitled 'Notes on the Early Life of Donne' (*Review
of English Studies*, 1927) where he establishes that "Donne
may have been born towards the end of 1571, or between
January and June 19, 1572…But it is certain that the poet
was born before June 19, 1572."

J. B.

November 1956

PREFACE TO
THE THIRD EDITION

VERY little change has been made in this edition in
chapters I to VII, but chapter VIII is entirely new.
It has long been recognized that Marvell's poetry
belongs to what Professor George Williamson called 'The
Donne tradition'[1] and, when a third edition of *Four Metaphysical Poets* was planned, I was glad to add a chapter on
Marvell and to change the title accordingly.

On first acquaintance readers may be more struck by
difference than by resemblance between Marvell and the
other four poets. This is because the first impression made
by poetry is, and should be, aural. In his lyrical poems
Marvell's phrasing is subservient to metre and the ear
catches the tune easily, especially as the verse patterns
include frequent and firmly stressed rhymes. And yet, as
I hope to show, if we retain the word 'metaphysical' as a
label for a poetic tradition, it is as appropriate to Marvell
as to Vaughan, and more so than to Crashaw.

Donne, Herbert, Vaughan and Marvell are markedly
individual poets, but all assume certain things about their
readers. They assume that they will have active minds, that
they will expect poems to be both complex and lucid, and
that they will be familiar with ideas that were current
among educated men of their time. Crashaw has always
seemed to me to fit uneasily into any account I could give
of this tradition (however, in the 1930's when the book was
first written, he was commonly thought of as a metaphysical poet). Professor Douglas Bush,[2] in 1962, suggests

---

[1] *The Donne Tradition. A Study of English Poetry from Donne to the
death of Cowley*, by George Williamson. Harvard University Press, 1930.
[2] *English Literature in the Earlier Seventeenth Century, 1600–1660*, by
Douglas Bush. Second Edition. Clarendon Press, 1962.

that his poetry is a good illustration of 'the elusive concept of baroque', and he describes Crashaw's 'bizarre intricacy of sensuous decoration and symbolic metaphor, a kind of form—or formlessness—which sought a unity deeper and higher than the classical, through emotional and impressionistic multiplicity'. Marvell, on the contrary, is the most classical of these five poets; Professor Bush calls him 'the finest flower of secular and serious metaphysical poetry'. It seems therefore fitting that this book should begin with John Donne and close with Andrew Marvell.

JOAN BENNETT

March 1963

ACKNOWLEDGEMENTS

To acknowledge one's debts is not easy, not because one is insensible of them, but for two quite other reasons. When one begins to reflect, one is overwhelmed. What ideas has one, after all, which did not grow out of some conversation or some book? Every seed was planted, a few have borne fruit. But a worse perplexity follows. Is the harvest worthy of the husbandry? Who would care to own this crop?

It is best that no one should be implicated, no names mentioned. Where my creditors are printed books they will often be obvious, but my deepest debt is to a few friends who have been as candid in criticism as they have been generous in encouragement. To one of these,[1] had it been good enough, the book would have been dedicated. But for his optimism it would not have been begun; but for his untiring helpfulness it could not have been completed.

For permission to quote copyright poems I am obliged to the Oxford University Press for *The Caged Skylark*, *I wake and feel the fell of dark* and *Carrion Comfort* by G. M. Hopkins; to Messrs Burns, Oates and Washbourne, Ltd, and Mr Wilfred Meynell for an extract from *The Hound of Heaven* by Francis Thompson; to Messrs Faber and Faber, Ltd, and the author for an extract from *Ash Wednesday* by T. S. Eliot; to Messrs Macmillan and Co., Ltd, and the Trustees of the Hardy Estate for *Wives in the Sere* and *In Tenebris* by Thomas Hardy; and to Messrs Macmillan and Co., Ltd, and Mrs Yeats for *The Folly of being Comforted*, *That the Night Come* and *The Rose of the World*, by W. B. Yeats.

J. B.

[1] The debt I cryptically acknowledged in 1934 was to Mr George Rylands.

CONTENTS

CHAPTER I

INTRODUCTORY

The extent to which images are discordant depends upon the extent to which we unfold them, and that is wholly within the poet's control, for it in turn depends primarily upon the rhythm and tempo of the writing.

MIDDLETON MURRY, *Countries of the Mind*

Neither are these only similitudes, as men of narrow observation may conceive them to be, but the same footsteps of nature, treading or printing upon several subjects or matters.   FRANCIS BACON, *Advancement of Learning*

THE term *metaphysical*, as applied to a group of poets who wrote under the influence of John Donne, has been consecrated by use since Dryden first employed it, in his dedication to *A Discourse concerning the Original and Progress of Satire*. It is not altogether a happy term, since it gives the impression that metaphysical poetry discusses the nature of the universe, in short, that, as Dryden assures the Earl of Dorset, 'Donne perplexes the minds of the fair sex with nice speculations of philosophy, when he should engage their hearts and entertain them with the softnesses of love'. But Donne and the poets most influenced by him were not speculating about the nature of things as, for instance, Milton does in *Paradise Lost* or Pope in *The Essay on Man* or Tennyson in *In Memoriam* (for there is a similar motive in these three poems, despite all differences of temperament and of treatment). When Donne writes

> At the round earths imagin'd corners, blow
> Your trumpets, Angells, and arise, arise
> From death, you numberlesse infinities
> Of soules,...[1]

[1] *Holy Sonnet* VII.

or even

> And new Philosophy calls all in doubt,
> The Element of fire is quite put out;
> The Sun is lost, and th'Earth, and no mans wit
> Can well direct him where to looke for it[1]

he is not defining the doctrine of the church about immortality or describing the new cosmology, he is expressing
a state of mind by referring to a background of ideas. He is
no more a philosophical poet because he makes use of ideas
than Shelley is a descriptive poet because he makes use of
things seen:

> The brightness
> Of her divinest presence trembles through
> Her limbs, as underneath a cloud of dew
> Embodied in the windless heaven of June
> Amid the splendour-wingéd stars, the moon
> Burns inextinguishably beautiful.
> And from her lips as from a hyacinth full
> Of honey-dew, a liquid murmur drops
> Killing the sense with passion.[2]

Shelley is not describing stars, moon, hyacinths or dew-
drops; he is using them to express his sensation about Emily.
Donne is not discussing whether the world is round or flat,
nor the validity of the 'new philosophy'; he is using these
exciting speculations to express and define his emotion. In
the sonnet it concerns death, judgment and eternity; in the
poem it is summed up in the subtitle:

By occasion of the untimely death of Mistress Elizabeth
Drury, the frailty and decay of this whole World is represented.

Nevertheless, Shelley used his method because he was
acutely aware of sense-impressions, and Donne his, because
he was acutely aware of the current of ideas. The word
'metaphysical' refers to style, rather than subject-matter;
but style reflects an attitude to experience. Experience to
the metaphysical poets was, as it were, grist to an intel-

---

[1] *An Anatomie of the World, The first Anniversary*, ll. 205 ff.
[2] *Epipsychidion.*

2

lectual mill. They looked for a connection between their emotion and mental concepts. All poetical imagery arises from a perceived likeness between different things; it may be as simple as

> One ask'd me where the Roses grew?
> I bade him not goe seck;
> But forthwith bade my *Julia* shew
> A bud in either cheek.[1]

where the relation is merely a similarity in colour, touch and perhaps scent, or it may be as complex as this:

> She lived in storm and strife,
> Her soul had such desire
> For what proud death may bring
> That it could not endure
> The common good of life,
> But lived as 'twere a king
> That packed his marriage day
> With banneret and pennon,
> Trumpet and kettledrum,
> And the outrageous cannon,
> To bundle time away
> That the night come.[2]

where a rich variety of relations is implied, relations between human effort towards an abstract good and the pomp, power and cruelty of kingship, things that lead away from the common joys; and again relations between death and the consummation of a marriage. The peculiarity of the metaphysical poets is not that they relate, but that the relations they perceive are more often logical than sensuous or emotional, and that they constantly connect the abstract with the concrete, the remote with the near, and the sublime with the commonplace.

Metaphysical poetry usually comprises an analysis as well as a correlation of emotions. A poet like Herrick, conscientious as an artist, but, as a man, apparently free

[1] Herrick.   [2] W. B. Yeats, *That the Night Come.*

from disturbing self-awareness, was unaffected by Donne's influence. He sang of his religion with untroubled simplicity:

> When the Tempter me pursu'th
> With the sins of all my youth,
> And halfe damns me with untruth;
>   Sweet Spirit comfort me!
>
> When the flames and hellish cries
> Fright mine eares, and fright mine eyes,
> And all terrors me surprise;
>   Sweet Spirit comfort me!
>
> When the Judgment is reveal'd
> And that open'd which was seal'd,
> When to Thee I have appeal'd;
>   Sweet Spirit comfort me![1]

The simplicity of rhythm and diction reflect Herrick's ease of mind. Donne's *Hymn to God the Father*, in contrast, with its meditative rhythm and its punning conclusion, communicates the self-mistrust of the more intellectual poet.

> Wilt thou forgive that sinne where I begunne,
>   Which was my sin, though it were done before?
> Wilt thou forgive that sinne; through which I runne,
>   And do run still: though still I do deplore?
>   When thou hast done, thou hast not done,
>   For, I have more.
>
> Wilt thou forgive that sinne which I have wonne
>   Others to sinne? and, made my sinne their doore?
> Wilt thou forgive that sinne which I did shunne
>   A yeare, or two: but wallowed in, a score?
>   When thou hast done, thou hast not done,
>   For I have more.
>
> I have a sinne of feare, that when I have spunne
>   My last thred, I shall perish on the shore;
> But sweare by thy selfe, that at my death thy sonne
>   Shall shine as he shines now, and heretofore;
>   And, having done that, Thou haste done,
>   I feare no more.

[1] *His Letanie, to the Holy Spirit.*

4

The poets who wrote successfully in the metaphysical style were all of them self-conscious and analytic, though they vary greatly in the range and depth of their thinking and in the subtlety of their self-knowledge. Donne, for instance, links up a wider range of ideas and explores a more complex attitude of mind in 'Batter my heart' than Herbert does in *Affliction*, while Herbert's *Affliction* is more subtle and self-aware than Vaughan's *Distraction*; but all three are analyses of emotion. They have in common sufficient detachment from an experience, at first intensely felt, to be intellectually aware of its intricacy.

Because of this analytic habit, the metaphysical poets preferred to use words which call the mind into play, rather than those that appeal to the senses or evoke an emotional response through memory. Commonly the reverberations, or overtones, of words in poetry depend very largely on the memory of sense-impressions they call up, or else on the memory of emotions that the same word has evoked in other contexts.

> No nightingale did ever chaunt
> More welcome notes to weary bands
> Of travellers in some shady haunt,
> Among Arabian sands:
>
> A voice so thrilling ne'er was heard
> In spring-time from the cuckoo-bird,
> Breaking the silence of the seas
> Among the farthest Hebrides.[1]

Unthinkingly the reader responds: the nightingale, Arabian sands, spring-time and the cuckoo-bird, silent seas, the farthest Hebrides; such words quicken emotions which lie dormant. They awaken both sense-memories and memories of a literary heritage. The metaphysical poets usually neglect this accumulated treasure. If they evoke memories, they are of 'large draughts of intellectual day' imbibed from science rather than from poetry.

[1] Wordsworth, *The Solitary Reaper*.

5

> Let Maps to other, worlds on worlds have showne
> Let us possesse one world, each hath one, and is one.[1]

or,

> Of what supreme almightie power
> Is thy great arm, which spans the east and west,
> And tacks the centre to the sphere![2]

or,

> (Though Loves whole World on us doth wheel.)[3]

We recognize that the words in such lines as these have more than their normal prose meaning; they reverberate as surely as do the 'Arabia', the 'Hebrides' and the 'cuckoo' of Wordsworth, but their stimulus is applied, not directly to the senses or the emotions, but to something more akin to the faculty that apprehends a mathematical problem.

> The whole Creation shakes off night
> And for thy shadow looks, the light;

writes Vaughan in *The Dawning*, an intellectual conceit, and one that sums up the metaphysical approach to experience. It would not be wide of the mark to describe metaphysical poetry as poetry written by men for whom the light of day is God's shadow. The description would apply to some secular metaphysical poems as well as to religious; it underlies Donne's

> But since my soule, whose child love is,
> Takes limmes of flesh, and else could nothing doe,
> More subtile then the parent is,
> Love must not be, but take a body too,...[4]

as clearly as it underlies Herbert's description of dead bodies as

> The shells of fledge souls left behinde,...

An intellectual bias affects not only the choice of words and images, but the form of their poems and their rhythmi-

---

[1] Donne, *The Good-Morrow.*   [2] Herbert, *Prayer.*
[3] Marvell, *The Definition of Love.*   [4] Donne, *Aire and Angels.*

cal effects. Here are two poets writing in the same age and
on the same theme; the first is from Nashe's play *Summer's
Last Will and Testament*:

> Beauty is but a flower
> Which wrinkles will devour:
> Brightness falls from the air,
> Queens have died young and fair;
> Dust hath closed Helen's eye:
> I am sick, I must die
>   Lord have mercy upon us!
>
> Strength stoops unto the grave:
> Worms feed on Hector brave;
> Swords may not fight with fate;
> Earth still holds ope her gate;
> Come! Come! the bells do cry.
> I am sick, I must die
>   Lord have mercy upon us!

The second is Donne's sixth *Holy Sonnet*:

> This is my playes last scene, here heavens appoint
> My pilgrimages last mile; and my race
> Idly, yet quickly runne, hath this last pace,
> My spans last inch, my minutes latest point,
> And gluttonous death, will instantly unjoynt
> My body, and soule, and I shall sleepe a space,
> But my'ever-waking part shall see that face,
> Whose feare already shakes my every joynt:
> Then, as my soule, to'heaven her first seate, takes flight,
> And earth-born body, in the earth shall dwell,
> So, fall my sinnes, that all may have their right,
> To where they'are bred, and would presse me, to hell.
> Impute me righteous, thus purg'd of evill,
> For thus I leave the world, the flesh, the devill.

Donne's pattern is the pattern of thought, of a mind
moving from the contemplation of a fact to deduction from
a fact and thence to a conclusion. The framework of the
poem is logical. Nashe's pattern is a symmetrical design
without development. Just as different is the function of

rhythm in the two poems. Nashe excites emotion by the 'dying fall' of his music:

> Come! Come! the bells do cry.
> I am sick, I must die
>> Lord have mercy upon us!

Donne appeals through the ear to the intellect. The repeated 'lasts' of the first four lines are the hammer strokes of finality; in the third line the contrast between narrow vowels and disyllables in the first half, and open vowelled monosyllables in the second half:

> Idly, yet quickly runne, hath this last pace,

expresses the contrasted feeling. The required sense of climax is furthered in line seven by the elision, arresting ear and tongue so that the mind may dwell on the terrific fact:

> But my'ever-waking part *shall see that face*,

the same close co-operation exists between meaning and sound in

> And earth-born body, in the earth shall dwell,

with its heavy succession of monosyllables and the emphasis thrown on the verb, and in line twelve contempt for sins is expressed in the narrow monosyllables:

> To *where* they'are *bred*, and would *presse* me, to *hell*.

Such is the part played by the ear in good metaphysical poetry. And the imagery is similarly arresting. Instead of touching the old springs of sorrow it sets the mind to work anew. It is his own horror of death that Donne is concerned with. 'Gluttonous' death, waiting to 'unjoint' soul and body, like a hungry animal watching for prey:

> Queens have died young and fair;
> Dust hath closed Helen's eye:
>
>> . . . . .
>
> Worms feed on Hector brave.

Nashe enriches his poem with the emotions with which these names are stored. We feel the pity of the general

8

fate. But Donne is contemplating himself in the moment of agony; it is his own peculiar sense of death that we share, and to do so we must follow the movement of his mind.

In metaphysical poetry emotions are shaped and expressed by logical reasoning, and both sound and picture are subservient to this end. Words consecrated to poetry are avoided *because* such words have accumulated emotion. The very reasons that prompt other poets to use these words, persuade Donne and his disciples to neglect them. Like Wordsworth they prefer words in everyday use; but their practice goes even further than his theory. Wordsworth proposed to use 'the natural language of impassioned feeling'.[1] But the metaphysical poets use the natural language of men when they are soberly engaged in commerce or in scientific speculation, so that the words themselves, apart from their meaning in the context, have no repercussions. They cut themselves off from one of the common means of poetry and thus become entirely dependent on a successful fusion between thought and feeling; they seldom employ easy or emotionally exciting rhythms (though these are more frequent in Vaughan and Crashaw than in Donne and Herbert). Often the rhythm is as intricate as the thought and only reveals itself when the emphasis has been carefully distributed accordingly to the sense; its function is that of a stimulant, not a narcotic, to the intellect. Elizabethan rhythms were usually suggested by a classical heritage, or by the requirements of music. The rhythms of Donne and his followers are dictated by the meaning.

These peculiarities of attitude and of style have a specific value. It is not only that, as Dr Johnson said, 'to write on their plan it was at least necessary to read and think', it is perhaps even more important that it was necessary to connect, and that the same difficult achievement is required

[1] The quotation is from Coleridge's *Biographia Literaria*, Ch. XVII; but it summarizes quite justly the gist of what Wordsworth says about poetic diction in his preface to the second edition of *Lyrical Ballads*.

of the reader. Successful reading of metaphysical poetry necessitates at least a temporary conquest of the tendency to divorce feeling from intelligence, to be moved only at the cost of being unable to judge, and to judge well only when the sympathies are not engaged. The incompatibility of detachment and participation, or amusement and pity, is constantly impoverishing our experiences. To some extent all good literature militates against this. Any poet must separate himself from his experience if his poem is to be more than a personal outcry, and to read any good poetry exercises both judgment and sensibility. But the metaphysical poets call upon the powers of connecting in a peculiar degree; they, more than most, answer to Mr Eliot's description of a poet as one who is 'constantly amalgamating disparate experiences', who 'is always forming new wholes' out of matter so diverse as 'reading Spinoza, falling in love and smelling the dinner cooking'.[1]

The search for the intellectual equivalents of emotion enforces connection and it also ensures detachment. To be handled by the intellect an experience must be held at arm's length.

> But O alas, so long, so farre
>   Our bodies why doe wee forbeare?
> They are ours, though they are not wee, Wee are
>   The intelligences, they the spheare.
> We owe them thankes, because they thus,
>   Did us, to us, at first convay,
> Yeelded their forces, sense, to us,
>   Nor are drosse to us, but allay.[2]

Contrast the private anguish of Keats' posthumous lines:

> You say you love; but then your hand
>   No soft squeeze for squeeze returneth,
> It is like a statue's, dead,—
>   While mine to passion burneth—
>   O love me truly![3]

[1] *Homage to John Dryden.* Hogarth Press, 1924.
[2] *The Extasie.*   [3] *Stanzas*, stanza IV.

Donne transmutes the personal experience of the lover into an affirmation about the nature of man. Without forfeiting the power to express emotion, the metaphysical style distances the merely personal; it is not true of the protagonist alone, but of all mankind that body and spirit are interdependent. The two intellectual conceits point to this conclusion.

While to its admirers the metaphysical style seems to have peculiar merits, its detractors have naturally laid emphasis on its peculiar faults. It has been attacked mainly for two reasons. First, it is objected, such a style soon degenerates into the pursuit of logical ingenuity for its own sake. This is certainly the fate that overtakes it when the poet has little to say. But it is at least no worse than the pursuit of sensation for its own sake. If Donne is more ingenious than effective in *The Flea*, it may be answered that Shelley is more sensational than effective in much of *The Revolt of Islam*, and that of the two *The Flea* is the more entertaining. The second objection is that the metaphysical style is needlessly obscure. It is a more ambiguous charge, because the word obscure has such diverse meanings. It is sometimes meant that the intellectual imagery fails to communicate the poet's emotion. It is impossible to generalize as to how far, in such cases, the reader or the poet is to blame. There may actually be a cleavage between the poet's image and his original impulse; on the other hand the reader may have been unwilling or unable to make the necessary intellectual effort. The mere novelty of the problem, to those accustomed to other kinds of poetry, is an obstacle. In Wordsworth's phrase: 'the poet must create the taste by which he is to be judged.' The metaphysical poets demand a continual breakdown of mental habits—experiences which have been kept apart in the mind are suddenly yoked together. This often occasions what seems like obscurity in a poem, but is really only an obstruction in the reader's mind. A different cause of obscurity is the fact that some images, which were clear to the poet's contemporaries, now need elucidation. Recondite imagery is a common cause of difficulty in poetry; but a difference should be made between the almost impassable obstacle of private symbolism, such as Blake uses in his Prophetic Books, or even imagery derived from individual literary pursuits, such as Mr Eliot uses in *The Waste Land* and, to a lesser degree, in *Ash Wednesday*; and the imagery of a poet like Donne, which demands only an acquaintance with widespread contemporary ideas.[1] Apart from unwonted connections and recondite imagery, poetry may be obscure through compression. Both Donne and Herbert offend in this, but their very careful punctuation usually makes the sense unambiguous. No one would contend that they are easily read; but then few suppose that easy accessibility is essential, or even common in good poetry. A variety of difficulties are admissible, provided they serve a purpose and that to overcome them affords, not only the pleasure of a victory, but the more lasting delight of a new experience.

[1] For example, in the stanza quoted from *The Extasie*, 'Wee are The intelligences, they the spheare', depends upon the doctrine of the old astronomy which taught that the heavenly bodies revolved round the earth in concentric spheres, each governed by an Intelligence.

CHAPTER II

JOHN DONNE, 1571[1]–1631

The greatest difference between the poet and the ordinary person is found, as has often been pointed out, in the range, delicacy, and freedom of the connections he is able to make between different elements of his experience.

I. A. RICHARDS, *Principles of Literary Criticism*

B Y the time Donne began to write, the Petrarchan fashion had had its day. He was by no means the first to feel restive about it; Sir John Davies had written his *Gulling Sonnets*, others, and Shakespeare among them, had challenged and reversed the conventional pose of self-depreciation and adulation of the mistress. There was, for the moment, little more to be said about love in those terms. But there was still much to be said about love. Donne experienced that 'human bondage' in most of its forms and he extended the range of lyrical expression to give tongue to what he suffered and enjoyed. The precise relation of his poetry to his biography is insoluble and not very important; what matters is that he knew enough to portray and analyse a wider range of emotion than any other English poet except Shakespeare. His *Songs and Sonets* and the *Elegies* may be dramatic or they may be subjective, more probably they are a mixture of the two, for experience and detachment are equally essential to a poet. Donne had enough experience to realize love's many moods, from the most brutally cynical to the most idealistic, and enough dramatic power to escape from the limits of anecdote into the expanses of poetry. That he scorned, hated, lusted after, loved, worshipped, there can be little doubt for anyone who has read his poetry; and

[1] See p. vi.

his biography confirms it. To conjecture that particular poems belong to particular episodes is a fascinating pursuit, but it has been too much indulged in. It has led to few certainties and cannot in any case do much to increase appreciation of the poetry. To enjoy that, it is only necessary to be prepared for a strange assortment of moods, to enter into each without reserve, and one thing further. Donne's reader must share, in some degree, his own capacity for associating widely diverse themes and feelings. He travelled from one type of experience to another, but carried with him into the new a vivid memory of what the old had felt like. When, for instance, after his wife's death he sought a church as the object of his devotion, the traditional image of the Bride of Christ fused itself in his mind with memories of secular love. Beseeching God to reveal the true Church he wrote:

> Betray kind husband thy spouse to our sights,
> And let myne amorous soule court thy mild Dove,
> Who is most trew, and pleasing to thee, then
> When she'is embrac'd and open to most men.[1]

The paradox was vividly realized in these terms by one who had formerly described a man committed

> To paths in love so dark, so dangerous:
> And those so ambush'd round with household spies,
> And over all, thy husbands towring eyes
> That flam'd with oylie sweat of jealousie.[2]

Other poets of his time emphasized the sharp divorce between their secular and sacred verses. They represented themselves as rejecting and despising their youth; but Donne recognized the unity of his experience. In *The Good-Morrow* he told his beloved

> If ever any beauty I did see,
> Which I desir'd, and got, 'twas but a dreame of thee.

and later he declared

> Here the admyring her my mind did whett
> To seeke thee God; so streames do shew their head;[3]

[1] *Holy Sonnet* XVIII.   [2] *Elegie* XII, ll. 41 ff.   [3] *Holy Sonnet* XVII.

and was not afraid to look back before the time when he
devoted himself to Anne More, to earlier days when he
could 'love both faire and browne'.

> As humorous is my contritione
> As my prophane Love, and as soone forgott:
> As ridlingly distemper'd, cold and hott,
> As praying, as mute; as infinite, as none.[1]

The same sense of connection enabled him to pass from
the trivial to the sublime, or from jest to earnest, with an
abruptness often disconcerting to readers of Milton and
Wordsworth. He may begin with the magnificence of

> At the round earths imagin'd corners, blow
> Your trumpets, Angells, and arise, arise
> From death, you numberlesse infinities
> Of soules, and to your scattered bodies goe,[2]

and continue by cataloguing a motley assortment of human
ills:
> All whome warre, dearth, age, agues, tyrannies,
> Despaire, law, chance, hath slaine....

It is an essential character of his mind that he recognizes
trivial mundane affairs as part of the same experience as
death and the dread of eternity. The tendency to segregate
the sublime from the commonplace is a form of romantic
idealization, more characteristic of the eighteenth and nineteenth than of the sixteenth and seventeenth centuries.

After the flood of conventional sonnet sequences in the
Petrarchan fashion, poets felt the need of realism. When
realism is sought as an escape from idealization, it often
leads to cynicism. One affectation is replaced by its opposite. Some of Donne's poems, like his prose *Paradoxes
and Problems* (which were described by John Donne the
younger as 'the entertainments of the author's youth'), are
the products of this reaction. Their characteristics are
intellectual exuberance and a spirit of contradiction. Both
prose and verse writings in this mood are exercises in moral

[1] *Ibid.* xix.   [2] *Ibid.* vii.

paradox, which compensate for cold affectation by bright wit and ingenious logic.

That Women are Inconstant, I with any man confess, but that Inconstancy is a bad quality, I against any man will maintain: For everything as it is one better than another, so it is fuller of *change*; The *Heavens* themselves continually turn, the *Stars* move, the *Moon* changeth; *Fire* whirleth, *Aire* flyeth, *Water* ebbs and flowes, the face of the *Earth* altereth her looks, *time* staies not; the Colour that is most light, will take most dyes: so in Men, they that have the most reason are the most alterable in their designes, and the darkest or most ignorant, do seldomest change; therefore Women changing more than Men, have also most *Reason*.[1]

The prose style is Euphuistic; characterized by balanced clauses and an accumulation of analogies. Donne has his tongue in his cheek; none the less his observation about the constancy of fools and the vacillations of the wise carries conviction. He is a shrewd observer and even his lightest writings are apt to contain these flashes of insight. The *Paradoxes* are a series of challenges thrown out to the morally conventional; poems in the same temper and using logic in a similar way are *The Indifferent*, *Confined Love*, *Womans constancy*, *The Flea* and others. In a sense they are as artificial as many an Elizabethan sonnet sequence; but at least Donne is adopting his own pose and not another's. Moreover, it is a pose which involves facing facts, if only some facts, perhaps those of which the poet was as yet aware, such as that

> Chang'd loves are but chang'd sorts of meat,
> And when hee hath the Kernell eate,
> Who doth not fling away the shell?[2]

Presently either the pose of cynicism gave place to genuine bitterness as the outcome of experience, or an increased mastery of his craft enabled Donne to express himself more convincingly. Some of the *Elegies* (I, II, IV and

---

[1] *Paradoxes and Problems*, No. 1.   [2] *Communitie*.

XII for instance) and such poems as *Loves Alchymie*, and *The Apparition*, have a convincing brutality not felt in the mocking tones of 'Goe and catch a falling starre' or 'I can love both faire and browne'. Jingling tunes and specious arguments are the expression and probably the outcome of lightheartedness. When he wrote like that Donne was impudent and unperturbed. In *The Apparition*, on the contrary, there is every sign of controlled passion; he governs every inflection so as to convey the cold rage of thwarted lust:

> When by thy scorne, O murdresse, I am dead,
> And that thou thinkst thee free
> From all solicitation from mee,
> Then shall my ghost come to thy bed,
> And thee, fain'd vestall, in worse armes shall see;
> Then thy sicke taper will begin to winke,
> And he, whose thou art then, being tyr'd before,
> Will, if thou stirre, or pinch to wake him, thinke
>   Thou call'st for more,
> And in false sleepe will from thee shrinke,
> And then poore Aspen wretch, neglected thou
> Bath'd in a cold quicksilver sweat wilt lye
>   A veryer ghost then I;
> What I will say, I will not tell thee now,
> Lest that preserve thee'; and since my love is spent,
> I'had rather thou shouldst painfully repent,
> Then by my threatnings rest still innocent.

The interplay of sound and meaning is masterly; the smooth, lingering sibilants of 'solicitation' surrounded by hard monosyllables—scorne, ghost, dead, bed—matching the contrast between what she expects and what he intends; the narrow vowels, like dagger thrusts—sicke, pinch, winke, thinke, shrinke—and the snarling rhymes at the end—spent, repent, innocent. Control of the sound pattern is no less potent in producing the total effect than is the vividness of the picture presented to the mind's eye, the 'sicke taper', the 'cold quicksilver sweat', or than is the brutal conception of the situation. There are qualities in this poem

17

and in the corresponding elegies which were new to English lyrical poetry, though not to the drama. The facts with which they deal are ugly; but they are faced and handled with unsparing realism. The poetry does not mitigate or disguise, it enforces the crudity of the situations it portrays.

> Fond woman, which would'st have thy husband die,
> And yet complain'st of his great jealousie;
> If swolne with poyson, hee lay in'his last bed,
> His body with a sere-barke covered,
> Drawing his breath, as thick and short, as can
> The nimblest crocheting Musitian,
> Ready with loathsome vomiting to spue
> His Soule out of one hell, into a new,
>
> .   .   .   .   .
>
> Thou would'st not weepe, but jolly,'and frolicke bee,
> As a slave, which to morrow should be free;
> Yet weep'st thou, when thou seest him hungerly
> Swallow his owne death, hearts-bane jealousie.[1]

A robust delight in dialectic is the most constant feature of Donne's poetry as of his prose. His intellectual ingenuity kept pace with his emotional development, but in the lighter poems there was often little else than logical dexterity, whereas in these elegies and poems it is subservient to another kind of excitement. Passion is conveyed in images as vivid as they are violent and in the skilful management of rhythm and tempo.

It is reasonable to conjecture, from the evidence of Donne's life and correspondence, that the poems just referred to were written before he met Anne More, who was to be his wife. But they may well have been written in the same years as another set of poems conceived in quite a different temper. These are the poems that record the poignant delight of mutual love-making, without reference to outside interference, and with no hint of inadequacy in the beloved. Typical poems in this mood are *The Sunne*

[1] *Elegie* I, *Jealosie*.

Rising, *The Dreame*, *The Breake of Day*. This last is the only one of Donne's poems that is put into the mouth of a woman and it is especially interesting for that reason. If he could imagine himself into the woman's part, he could no doubt also imagine himself into other situations which had no counterpart in real life. There is no need then to suppose that every poem had its corresponding anecdote; if *The Breake of Day* is the fruit of dramatic invention, so, probably, are many other poems, however realistic they may be.

The Sunne Rising is remarkable for its variety of tone, from the gay impertinence of its opening:

> Busie old foole, unruly Sunne,
> Why dost thou thus,
> Through windowes, and through curtaines call on us?
> Must to thy motions lovers seasons run?
> Sawcy pedantique wretch, goe chide
> Late schoole boyes and sowre prentices,
> Goe tell Court-huntsmen, that the King will ride,
> Call countrey ants to harvest offices;

to the full notes of satisfied love:

> Love, all alike, no season knowes, nor clyme,
> Nor houres, dayes, moneths, which are the rags of time.

and

> She'is all States, and all Princes, I,
> Nothing else is.

The poem is a successful fusion of wit and passion. *The Dreame*, on the other hand, is written in one key. The enjoyment of the act of love is the theme of both; the difference is that the first, through wit and raillery, takes cognizance of the outside world, while the second narrows the attention to its one object. To read the two side by side is to get a measure of Donne's variety of treatment; he rescued English love poetry from the monotony which was threatening to engulf it at the end of the sixteenth century.

Donne could handle sensual love in all its aspects, from the bitterness of desire thwarted, to the fleeting paradise of desire fulfilled. But he was to do more than this. There are a number of poems which celebrate that rarer love in which the senses are but vehicles and mating is a 'marriage of true minds'. There is still no certain means of judging to whom any given poem was addressed; but we know that his relation to Anne More was of this character. Thirteen years after his marriage to her he could write: 'We had not one another at so cheap a rate as that we should ever be weary of one another.' The sentence strikes the same note of security as distinguishes his most mature love poetry. The need for watchful jealousy passes when the fickle senses are no longer the foundation upon which love is built. To Donne this experience was like awakening from a nightmare: he cries

> And now good morrow to our waking soules,
> Which watch not one another out of feare;[1]

or he asserts that, after their death, he and his mistress will be thought of as

> You, to whom love was peace, that now is rage.[2]

This welcome to serenity is the counterpart of his former distrust, both of his own and of his mistress' constancy. His ardent and adventurous temperament craved a point of rest, first from the love of women and later from the love of God. The triumphant close of *The Anniversarie* is the assertion of a satisfied need:

> Who is so safe as wee? where none can doe
> Treason to us, except one of us two.
>   True and false feares let us refraine,
> Let us love nobly, and live, and adde againe
> Yeares and yeares unto yeares, till we attaine
> To write threescore: this is the second of our raigne.

[1] *The Good-Morrow.*   [2] *The Canonization.*

20

In this phase of experience Donne does not surprise us by
wit into the acceptance of a paradox; he progresses from
thought to thought with a measured and weighty music:

> Dull sublunary lovers love
>   (Whose soule is sense) cannot admit
> Absence, because it doth remove
>   Those things which elemented it.
>
> But we by a love, so much refin'd
>   That ourselves know not what it is,
> Inter-assured of the mind,
>   Care lesse, eyes, lips, and hands to misse.[1]

A new serenity is reflected in the texture of the verse.
There is no intellectual jugglery as in the earlier poems,
but a series of reasoned comparisons. Donne looks now
for intellectual figures analogous to an emotion which is
itself both felt and thought. *Aire and Angels* may not have
been addressed to his wife; but, by its intellectual music,
it belongs to the same period as the *Valedictions* and it
handles the same theme, the relation between body and soul
in sexual love:

> Twice or thrice had I loved thee,
> Before I knew thy face or name;
> So in a voice, so in a shapelesse flame,
> *Angells* affect us oft, and worship'd bee;
>   Still when, to where thou wert, I came,
> Some lovely glorious nothing I did see.
>   But since my soule, whose child love is,
> Takes limmes of flesh, and else could nothing doe,
>   More subtile then the parent is,
> Love must not be, but take a body too,
>   And therefore what thou wert, and who,
>   I bid Love aske, and now
> That it assume thy body, I allow,
> And fixe it selfe in thy lip, eye, and brow.
>
> Whilst thus to ballast love, I thought,
> And so more steddily to have gone,

---

[1] *A Valediction: forbidding mourning.*

With wares which would sinke admiration,
I saw, I had loves pinnace overfraught,
   Ev'ry thy haire for love to worke upon
Is much too much, some fitter must be sought;
   For, nor in nothing, nor in things
Extreme, and scatt'ring bright, can love inhere;
   Then as an Angell, face, and rings
Of aire, not pure as it, yet pure doth weare,
   So thy love may be my loves spheare;
         Just such disparitie
As is twixt Aire and Angells puritie,
'Twixt womens love, and mens will ever bee.

That is a difficult poem for the modern reader to understand; some have supposed that the closing couplet,
affirming as it does that woman's love is necessarily less
pure than man's, is an expression of cynicism. But it is
Donne's habit to strike his keynote in the first lines of a
poem; if the reader's final impression is in a different key,
he should suspect himself of misinterpreting. So when
Donne begins:

> Twice or thrice had I loved thee,
> Before I knew thy face or name;

we should expect a poem in the mood of *The Good-Morrow*
which contains the similar statement:

> If ever any beauty I did see,
> Which I desir'd, and got, t'was but a dreame of thee.

His cynical poems begin with such lines as

> I can love both faire and browne,

or, more bitterly:

> When by thy scorne, O murdresse, I am dead,

In the first stanza of *Aire and Angels* Donne is saying much
what he says in *The Extasie*, man is a body as well as a soul;

22

love is the child of the soul, but the soul itself can do nothing in this world without the body:

> More subtile then the parent is,
> Love must not be, but take a body too,

Therefore the god of love is asked to find out who or what is the 'lovely glorious nothing'. And the god shows Donne his fair mistress, such as Elizabethan sonneteers described, with her 'lip, eye and brow'.

But, in the second stanza, Donne rejects the lady's physical charms as the object of his love. He uses a metaphor in which his love is a ship and he is looking for wares to ballast it. His admiration (wonder) is the keel; but the lady's physical charms instead of making the keel ride steadily through the water will be likely to sink the ship. He decides that love can no more reside in every bright hair of his mistress's head than in 'some lovely glorious nothing'. He then introduces the figure that gives the poem its title. Angels, in medieval angelology, manifested themselves to men by assuming 'wings and face of aire' the most suitable of the four elements. Yet air, since it is a terrestrial element is less pure than the angel in its supernatural state. The lady's love for him, Donne is saying, can embody his love for her as the air embodies the angel. It will be a sphere in which his love will rule as intelligences rule the heavenly spheres. In the 'great chain of being', reaching down from God to the lowest of His creatures, woman is next below man, just as the human pair are above animals, vegetable life and minerals, that is why the woman's love is as much less ethereal than the man's as air is less ethereal than angelic substance. The man's love as described in the first stanza was aspiration after the ideal, he has now found that ideal manifested in the woman's love for him. The brilliant ingenuity displayed in such a poem as *The Flea* has developed into a logical subtlety capable of expressing complex emotion. Donne could by now conceive and express a love which, though it belongs as much to the body as to the mind, is strong in absence and even independent of external beauty. In *Elegie* v he leaves his picture with his mistress before going on a journey. When he returns the picture may be no likeness:

> If rivall fooles taxe thee to'have lov'd a man,
> So foule, and course, as, Oh, I may seeme than,
> This shall say what I was: and thou shalt say,
> Doe his hurts reach mee? doth my worth decay?
> Or doe they reach his judging minde, that hee
> Should now love lesse, what hee did love to see?
> That which in him was faire and delicate,
> Was but the milke, which in loves childish state
> Did nurse it: who now is growne strong enough
> To feed on that, which to disused tasts seemes tough.

The relation between mind and body, the security of a love in which that relation has been fully established, and the unity of lovers are the themes of Donne's maturity. They are themes which concern all lovers and they refute the implication of Dryden's famous criticism. Dryden's picture of Donne who 'perplexes the minds of the fair sex with nice speculations of philosophy'[1] is profoundly misleading. He may use such speculations as an instrument; but his own inquiries in his poetry are about love itself:

> Me thinkes I lyed all winter, when I swore,
> My love was infinite, if spring make'it more.[2]

or

> Thou canst not every day give me thy heart,
> If thou canst give it, then thou never gavest it.[3]

'The metaphysics' occur in his poetry as a vehicle, but never as the thing conveyed.

Before and during his married years Donne enjoyed the friendship of women and these friendships gave rise to a

---

[1] Dedication to *A Discourse concerning the Original and Progress of Satire.*
[2] *Loves growth.*   [3] *Lovers infinitenesse.*

number of poems concerning a relation between man and woman in which, for some reason, physical union is denied. In *The Undertaking* he claims such a relation as an ideal, desirable in itself, but beyond the reach of most men:

> If, as I have, you also doe
>   Virtue'attir'd in woman see,
> And dare love that, and say so too,
>   And forget the Hee and Shee;
>
> .   .   .   .   .
>
> Then you have done a braver thing
>   Than all the *Worthies* did;
> And a braver thence will spring,
>   Which is, to keep that hid.

More often he is disturbed by the sense of incompleteness. His intellect rebels against the restraint that has been imposed. He claims to have obeyed the rules, but not to have accepted them:

> Comming and going, wee
> Perchance might kisse, but not between those meales;
>   Our hands ne'r toucht the seales,
> Which nature, injur'd by late law, sets free: [1]

The parenthesis in the last quoted line sounds the note of rebellion. In *Twickenham Garden* he complains more bitterly against the impossibility of possessing his beloved; the last couplet is his grudging acceptance of the facts:

> O perverse sexe, where none is true but shee,
>   Who's therefore true, because her truth kills mee.

In *The Blossome* he proposes to wean his heart from an unyielding lover and to give it

> ...to another friend, whom wee shall finde
> As glad to have my body, as my minde.

Unlike Herbert, Vaughan and Crashaw, Donne never, even in his religious poetry, belittled physical love; no poet has paid more consistent homage to a complete human relationship.

---

[1] *The Relique.*

After his wife's death he sought in religion for the sense of security and completeness that she had at one time given him. Religion had always been of great intellectual interest for him. Born and bred a Roman Catholic he accepted the Church of England (outside of which all preferment in church or state was barred to him), but not without a struggle. In *Satyre* III, written between 1593 and 1595, he considers the relative claims of nonconformity, Anglicanism and Roman Catholicism. Already religion and the search for the true church are of grave importance to him:

> ...though truth and falsehood bee
> Neare twins, yet truth a little elder is;
> Be busie to seeke her, beleeve mee this,
> Hee's not of none, nor worst, that seekes the best.
> To adore, or scorne an image, or protest,
> May all be bad; doubt wisely; in strange way
> To stand inquiring right, is not to stray;
> To sleepe, or runne wrong, is. On a huge hill,
> Cragged, and steep, Truth stands, and hee that will
> Reach her, about must, and about must goe;
> And what the hills suddennes resists, winne so;
> Yet strive so, that before age, deaths twilight,
> Thy Soule rest, for none can worke in that night.

In the *Holy Sonnets* the desire for intellectual rest is interwoven with a need for the emotional serenity he had tasted in marriage. He cries out to God in the accents of love:

> Take mee to you, imprison mee, for I
> Except you'enthrall mee, never shall be free,
> Nor ever chast, except you ravish mee.[1]

He expresses his love for God in terms of that of a lover for his mistress, or, as here, a woman for her lover, he trusts and mistrusts God's pity as the lover vacillates between the secure sense of being loved and the recurrent fear that love may yet be withdrawn:

> What if this present were the worlds last night?
> Marke in my heart, O Soule, where thou dost dwell,

[1] *Holy Sonnet* XIV.

26

The picture of Christ crucified, and tell
Whether that countenance can thee affright,

.   .   .   .

No, no; but as in my idolatrie
I said to all my profane mistresses,
Beauty, of pitty, foulnesse onely is
A signe of rigour: so I say to thee,
To wicked spirits are horrid shapes assign'd,
This beauteous forme assures a pitious minde.[1]

In the religious poetry Donne explores his feelings towards
God just as, in the secular poetry, he explored his feelings
towards the beloved. He defines the intricate balance of
his attitude with similar subtlety, although, as already in
the mature love poetry, delight in paradox has given place
to the perception of interrelations. In the religious poetry,
as in the secular, profound emotion works upon Donne's
intellect not as a narcotic but as a stimulant.

The *Litany*, composed in 1609, must have been among
the earliest of Donne's religious poems. Sir Edmund Gosse
dismissed it as a 'cold work of the intellect', but its
measured tone is the result, not of coldness, but of the
marriage of thought and feeling. It has an intricate slow
music which suggests thinking aloud:

From being anxious, or secure,
Dead clods of sadnesse, or light squibs of mirth,
From thinking, that great courts immure
All, or no happinesse, or that this earth
Is only for our prison fram'd,
Or that thou art covetous
To them whom thou lovest, or that they are maim'd
From reaching this worlds sweet, who seek thee thus,
With all their might, Good Lord deliver us.

Balance and serenity is reflected in the quietness of the
rhythm, the struggle through which it has been achieved
is expressed in the close-packed thought. The mind of the

[1] *Ibid.* XIII.

reader is continually checked, not by the surprise of paradox but by the sense of balance and sufficiency upon which the mind pauses as thought after thought receives its complement:

> From needing danger, to bee good,
> From owing thee yesterdaies teares to day,
> From trusting so much to thy blood,
> That in that hope, wee wound our soule away,
> From bribing thee with Almes, to excuse
> Some sinne more burdenous,
> From light affecting, in religion, newes,
> From thinking us all soule, neglecting thus
> Our mutual duties, Lord deliver us.

This low-toned music, compelling the reader to adopt the deliberate pace of meditation without losing the rhythm of impassioned earnestness, is a rare achievement in poetry. Mr T. S. Eliot in *Ash Wednesday*, a poem whose mood of tranquillity after conflict is not unlike that of Donne's *Litany*, achieves by the movement of the verse a similar effect, as of emotion held in check and regulated by thought. Both poems are, of course, based on liturgical patterns:

> Consequently I rejoice, having to construct something
> Upon which to rejoice
>
> And pray to God to have mercy upon us
> And I pray that I may forget
> These matters that with myself I too much discuss
> Too much explain
> Because I do not hope to turn again
> Let these words answer
> For what is done, not to be done again
> May the judgement not be too heavy upon us
>
> Because these wings are no longer wings to fly
> But merely vans to beat the air
> The air which is now thoroughly small and dry
> Smaller and dryer than the will
> Teach us to care and not to care
> Teach us to sit still.

This rapid survey has attempted no more than an indication of the diversity of Donne's poetry. Because of the alternation of his moods and the range of his experience, and because his poems have inevitably been printed without reference to a chronological order, it seemed necessary to indicate the variety of tone and intention comprised in them, as a preliminary to a study of his poetic method.

CHAPTER III

DONNE'S TECHNICAL ORIGINALITY

Sensibility alters from generation to generation, whether we will or no, expression is only altered by a man of genius.

T. S. ELIOT

ONNE'S technique was in many ways a new thing in English poetry and his most important innovations, although they found imitators among his immediate successors, afterwards remained in abeyance for two centuries. The practice of Milton and his many imitators, of the eighteenth-century poets, or of the nineteenth century, with the exception of Gerard Manley Hopkins, show small trace of Donne's influence. Milton's Eve is

> Like a wood nymph light
> Oread or Dryad, or of Delia's train.

Burns sings of one of his lady-loves:

> I see her in the dewy flowers
> I see her sweet and fair:
> I hear her in the tunefu' birds,
> I hear her charm the air:

Shelley tells of

> A Lady the wonder of her kind,
> Whose form was upborne by a lovely mind
> Which, dilating, had moulded her mien and motion
> Like a sea-flower unfolded beneath the ocean.

However much they differ, these poets use what seems like the same language compared with Donne, who likens his mistress to a hemisphere or one arm of a pair of compasses, speaks of her hair as a viceroy and her tears as coins or maps.

Donne had a different conception of the function of imagery from that of these other poets. The purpose of an image in his poetry is to define the emotional experience by an intellectual parallel. It is as essential to follow his reasoning when reading, as it is to respond to Keats' sense perception of dethroned Saturn when

> Upon the sodden ground
> His old right hand lay nerveless, listless, dead,
> Unsceptred; and his realmless eyes were closed.

Keats' sensuous impression is identified with the thing he wants to express; Donne, on the other hand, identifies his intellectual analogy with his emotion. A great part of the value of his poetry, to those who enjoy him, lies in the demand he thus makes on the imagination in the sense in which Coleridge defines it: 'judgment ever awake and steady self-possession with enthusiasm and feeling profound or vehement.'[1]

Donne's reader must be capable, not only of feeling and thinking at the same time; but even of simultaneously sharing an emotion and enjoying a joke. He must move as easily as Donne himself from the mood of the first stanza of *The Sunne Rising* to that of the last; or from the sardonic temper of the opening lines of *The Relique* to the poignancy of what follows:

> When my grave is broke up againe
> Some second ghest to entertaine,
> (For graves have learn'd that woman-head
> To be to more then one a Bed)
> And he that digs it, spies
> A bracelet of bright haire about the bone,
> Will he not let'us alone,
> And thinke that there a loving couple lies,
> Who thought that this device might be some way
> To make their soules, at the last busie day,
> Meet at this grave, and make a little stay?

[1] *Biographia Literaria*, c. XIV.

31

The parenthesis is not irrelevant, it points the contrast between the common run of women and that 'not impossible she' whom he describes in the last lines:

> But now alas,
> All measure, and all language, I should passe,
> Should I tell what a miracle shee was.

His images are drawn from his own interests, so that he is always illustrating one facet of his experience by another. Everything that played an important part in his life or left its mark upon his mind occurs in the poetry, not as subject-matter, but as imagery. His subject-matter was, as has been seen, confined almost entirely to various aspects of love and of religion; but his imagery reveals the width of his intellectual explorations.

He was widely read in most of the subjects that excited cultivated minds in his day: astronomy, chemistry, geography, physiology, law, and theology, and he drew upon all these indifferently for illustration. Dr Johnson mitigates his strictures on the metaphysical poets by allowing that 'if their conceits were far-fetched they were often worth the carriage', but, in Donne's case at any rate, they were not far-fetched, they were a part of his everyday life. Today, there can be nothing to surprise us in a lively interest in astronomy; Copernicus, Kepler and Galileo were for Donne's contemporaries what Einstein is for us. The facts they were discovering about the universe affected thought as radically. The scepticism of the modern astronomers about law and logic in stellar movements, was paralleled in the seventeenth century by scepticism about the central position of the earth. In each case the new theory revolutionizes the conception of man's importance in relation to the whole. Donne might well assume that his readers would respond to imagery drawn from so vital an issue. He expressed no opinion as to the facts. Nowhere, either in verse or prose, does he argue about Ptolemaic or Copernican systems; he used either indifferently or the conflict between the two, for the expression of something else. In *An Anatomie of the World, The first Anniversary*, where, by occasion of the anniversary of the death of Elizabeth Drury, Donne mourns the decay of morals, he uses the new philosophy as an illustration. It is the symptom, perhaps partly the cause, of the breaking up of the medieval world-order:

> And new Philosophy calls all in doubt,
> The Element of fire is quite put out;
> The Sun is lost, and th'earth, and no mans wit
> Can well direct him where to looke for it.
> And freely men confesse that this world's spent,
> When in the Planets, and the Firmament
> They seeke so many new; they see that this
> Is crumbled out againe to his Atomies.
> 'Tis all in peeces, all cohaerence gone;
> All just supply, and all Relation:
> Prince, Subject, Father, Sonne, are things forgot,
> For every man alone thinkes he hath got
> To be a Phoenix, and that then can bee
> None of that kinde, of which he is, but hee.[1]

But more often, in his poetry, Donne draws his images from the old astronomy. In *Good Friday, 1613, Riding Westward* he used the scholastic doctrine of the spheres, each governed by an intelligence or angel;[2] and the Ptolemaic doctrine of cycles and epicycles:

> Let mans Soule be a Spheare, and then, in this,
> The intelligence that moves, devotion is,
> And as the other Spheares, by being growne
> Subject to forraigne motions, lose their owne,
> And being by others hurried every day,
> Scarce in a yeare their naturall forme obey:
> Pleasure or businesse, so, our Soules admit
> For their first mover, and are whirld by it.

[1] *An Anatomie of the World, The first Anniversary*, ll. 205 ff.

[2] The same doctrine of intelligences governing spheres is used in *The Extasie* and in *Aire and Angels*. It owed its origin to St Thomas Aquinas, though it was not rejected by Kepler. (See article on Astrology, *Enc. Brit.*)

Again in the *Valediction: forbidding mourning* he uses an old-fashioned Ptolemaic doctrine:

> Moving of th'earth brings harmes and feares,
> ~~Men reckon what it did and meant,~~
> But trepidation of the spheares,
> Though greater farre, is innocent.

whilst in a verse letter to Lady Bedford he adopts the new Copernican teaching about a moving earth and stationary sun. The poetry tells us nothing about Donne's intellectual attitude to astronomy, except that he was aware both of obsolete and of recent theories.

He drew as freely and, from a scientific point of view, as indiscriminately, on contemporary chemical ideas, making use of the latest scientific theory, or of current superstition, as each served his purpose. His various references to alchemy are typical. Sometimes he accepts it as valid, sometimes he assumes it is all imposture. In a verse letter *To the Countesse of Huntingdon* the doctrine of transubstantiation and the alchemical theory of the transmutation of metals together express the notion that the spirit of the dead has entered into the living. He is speaking of the Countess's sister recently dead:

> She guilded us: But you are gold, and Shee;
> Us she inform'd, but transubstantiates you;
> Soft dispositions which ductile bee,
> Elixarlike, she makes not cleane, but new.

In *An Anatomie of the World*, to describe Elizabeth Drury as immune from the stain of the fall, he speaks of her as

> ...She that could drive
> The poysonous tincture, and the staine of *Eve*,
> Out of her thoughts, and deeds; and purifie
> All, by a true religious Alchymie;[1]

In *Loves Alchymie*, on the other hand;

> Oh, 'tis imposture all:
> And as no chymique yet th'Elixar got,

[1] *The first Anniversary.*

34

But glorifies his pregnant pot,
If by the way to him befall
Some odoriferous thing, or medicinall,
So, lovers dreame a rich and long delight,
But get a winter-seeming summers night.

Increasing knowledge of the world's surface was causing
as much excitement as increasing knowledge of the Cosmos
in Donne's lifetime so that, as was to be expected, he
frequently made use of geographical images. Examples will
be found in *The Good-Morrow*; *A Valediction: Of the Booke*
(last stanza); *Hymn to God my God in my Sicknesse*; and in
An Anatomie of the World, The first Anniversary. As far as
the evidence of the poetry goes, Donne had no more and
no less knowledge of contemporary geographical theories
than an intelligent, well-read man today normally acquires
of astronomy or psychology; but, because all subjects
which invite the play of the mind were his delight, all such
subjects occur to him in his mood of poetic creation.

Donne's physiological imagery has caused more comment
than that drawn from other sciences, partly because of its
frequent occurrence, both in prose and verse, and partly
because it has aroused disgust in certain readers. He has
been accused of morbidness, a charge supported by his
elaborate preparations for his own funeral and his maso-
chistic dwelling in his last sermon on 'the wormes that shall
feed and feed sweetly upon us'. In the first place it must
be remembered that physiology at the beginning of the
seventeenth century was as unmapped and exciting a ter-
ritory as were astronomy and geography, or as psychology
is today. No one who has scanned the pages of Burton
will doubt its fertility. Mrs Simpson tells us in her *Study of
the Prose Works of John Donne* that, while he was studying
law, between 1590 and 1601, Donne also mastered 'the
grounds and use of physique'. His contemporary, Lord
Herbert of Cherbury, thought such study an essential part
of the education of a gentleman. Inevitably, living when

he did, and with his 'immoderate, hydroptique thirst for human learning', Donne was interested in medicine and inevitably, therefore, he made use of medical ideas to define his emotional experiences. Moreover, Donne's intellectual interest in medicine was probably re-enforced by the sorrows of his seventeen years of married life, during which several of his children died, he himself was repeatedly ill, and finally his wife died, worn out with poverty and sickness. It is no wonder that images from disease and dissolution haunt his later prose and verse. His desire for God is a dropsy:

> But though I have found thee, and thou my thirst
>   hast fed,
> A holy thirsty dropsy melts mee yett.[1]

The coming and going of his religious fervour is an ague:

> So my devout fitts come and go away
> Like a fantastique Ague: save that here
> Those are my best dayes, when I shake with feare.[2]

Two of his best known love poems have as their central symbol
> A bracelet of bright haire about the bone,

which will keep his skeleton from dissolution, or will be worshipped for a relic after his death.

But the prevalence of the facts of death and disease, both in his verse and in his prose, is not only due to an intellectual interest in physiology. It is the counterpart of his delight in the life of the senses. He is as medieval in his insistence on the grave and the narrow margin that divides the skeleton from the living face, as he is in his scholastic delight in the processes of reasoning. His is an attitude to the body that belongs to a time when death lurked round every corner, the gift of plague, famine or violence. Realistic and familiar treatment of the physical facts of death is not peculiar to Donne; it is the mark of his age, it

---

[1] *Holy Sonnet* XVII.   [2] *Holy Sonnet* XIX.

stamps the pages of Webster, of Burton, of Jeremy Taylor no less than Donne's own. The men of the Middle Ages and of the Renaissance knew that life is but a moment; they valued it the more highly and especially those aspects of it which vanish most certainly. The more the life of the senses is valued, the more terrible and insistent the fact of its transience becomes and also the physical incidence of death. One may thrust these down into the unconscious, but this was never Donne's way nor the way of his contemporaries. With him as with them a full rich physical life brought into prominence the fact of mortality, in a way which is perhaps less morbid than its opposite, the 'hush! hush!' attitude to disease and death.

The nature of Donne's imagery accounts for some of the strangeness felt by a modern reader who encounters his poetry for the first time. The nemesis of being very actual in one's own generation is often that one appears strange to those that succeed. But the difficulty of merely deciphering Donne's meaning has been much exaggerated. The force of his image is nearly always apparent from the context, even when the doctrine of which it forms a part is forgotten.[1] The real difficulty is not to discern what might be described as the 'prose meaning', but to allow an image, which must first be seized intellectually, subsequently to affect one's whole sensibility:

> Shee'is dead; And all which die
>   To their first Elements resolve;
> And wee were mutuall Elements to us,
>   And made of one another.
>   My body then doth hers involve,
> And those things whereof I consist, hereby
> In me abundant grow, and burdenous,
>   And nourish not, but smother.[2]

[1] At the worst this kind of difficulty, due to the reader's ignorance of contemporary ideas, can often be removed by a reference to Professor Grierson's notes in the Clarendon Press edition.

[2] *The Dissolution.*

To arrive at the meaning we need only know of the theory that death is the breaking up of a compound into its elements; a theory stated by the verse itself. But to arrive at the meaning is not the same as to experience the poem. When Hardy writes:

> Wintertime nighs;
> But my bereavement-pain
> It cannot bring again:
>   Twice no one dies.
>
>   Flower petals flee;
> But, since it once hath been,
> No more that severing scene
>   Can harrow me.
>
>   Birds faint in dread:
> I shall not lose old strength
> In the lone frost's black length:
>   Strength long since fled![1]

a train of emotionally relevant associations troop into the mind. Winter, the falling flowers, birds in bleak weather, frost and the blackened earth all echo the sense of bereavement. The images touch the same keys as the loss they represent, whereas Donne's analogy needs to be thought through to its consequences before we feel with him.

When Yeats in his early poetry (in his later poems he preferred a more austere and, in a sense, a more metaphysical style) required an hyperbole he made use of the reader's remembered emotions:

> Who dreamed that beauty passes like a dream?
> For these red lips with all their mournful pride,
> Mournful that no new wonder may betide,
> Troy passed away in one high funeral gleam,
> And Usna's children died.
>
>   .   .   .   .   .
>
> Bow down, archangels, in your dim abode:
> Before you were, or any hearts to beat,
> Weary and kind one lingered by His seat;
> He made the world to be a grassy road
> Before her wandering feet.[2]

[1] *In Tenebris*, first three stanzas.   [2] *The Rose of the World.*

All the sorrow and glory that adheres to the legends of Greece or of Ireland are used by the poet to evoke the state of mind he requires. Donne frequently employs the device of hyperbole; but it operates in a different way.

> O wrangling schooles, that search what fire
>   Shall burne this world, had none the wit
> Unto this knowledge to aspire,
>   That this her feaver might be it?[1]

Unless the image awakens some of the excitement about ideas which impelled the scholastic Fathers, Donne's reader will remain unmoved. It is not difficult to understand the stanza, it may be difficult to respond to it with the feeling the poem requires. Donne's images must be followed logically; point by point they fit the emotion illustrated. In *Loves growth*, for instance, in image after image Donne probes into a universal experience; descanting on the re-birth of love in the spring-time; asserting finally:

> And yet no greater, but more eminent,
>   Love by the spring is growne;
>   As, in the firmament,
> Starres by the Sunne are not inlarg'd but showne.
> Gentle love deeds, as blossomes on a bough,
> From loves awakened root do bud out now.
> If, as in water stir'd more circles bee
> Produc'd by one, love such additions take,
> Those like so many spheares, but one heaven make,
> For, they are all concentrique unto thee.
> And though each spring doe adde to love new heate,
> As princes doe in times of action get
> New taxes, and remit them not in peace,
> No winter shall abate the springs encrease.

The words which in other poetry would bring with them an aura of association and require no further reflection, such words as *starres*, *sunne*, *blossomes*, *spring*, *root*, and *bud*, operate differently in Donne's poem. We need to follow intellectually the relation of each to the subject. If we are to enjoy Donne, such activity must be in itself a delight.

[1] *A Feaver.*

The words which strike the keynote of the poem are *circles*, *spheares*, *concentrique*; these are the symbols of that infinity in love which underlies the human ebb and flow. The circle occurs again and again in Donne's verse and in his prose as the symbol of infinity. Insensibility to such intellectual symbolism has caused not only Dr Johnson but even so modern a critic as Miss Sackville-West to cite the compass image, in the *Valediction: forbidding mourning*, as an example of metaphysical ineptitude.[1]

We expect from poetry something which is often called 'verbal magic', whereby the single word, in its context, assumes a richer significance than that which ordinarily belongs to it. This is owing largely to the sequence of sounds; but also largely, in most poetry, to the associated memories of emotion and sensation that the word brings with it. Donne's words bring with them the memory of abstract ideas. The magical lines in his poetry are those which evoke such conceptions as those of space, time, nothingness, eternity:

> Let Maps to other, worlds on worlds have shown.[2]
>
> Love, all alike, no season knowes, nor clyme,
> Nor houres, dayes, moneths, which are the rags of time.[3]
>
> He ruin'd mee, and I am re-begot
> Of absence, darknesse, death; things which are not.[4]
>
> All changing unchang'd Antient of dayes.[5]

The lovely vowel music of this last line is certainly a part of its magic. It is rare for Donne to make this kind of use of his sound-pattern. His conception of rhythm was as original as his diction and imagery, and many critics, even down to our own times, have echoed Ben Jonson's judgment that 'Donne for not keeping of accent deserves hanging'.

---

[1] In her *Andrew Marvell*, Hogarth Press (The Poets on the Poets).
[2] *The Good-Morrow.* [3] *The Sunne Rising.*
[4] *A nocturnall upon S. Lucies day.* [5] *Holy Sonnets. La Corona.*

He forsook the simple tunes of the Elizabethans which dictate the accent of joy or sorrow:

> Love for such a cherry lip
> Would be glad to pawn his arrows;
> Venus here to take a sip
> Would sell her doves and team of sparrows.
>> But they shall not so;
>> Hey nonny, nonny no!
>> None but I this lip must owe,
>> Hey nonny, nonny no!

And the sad cadences of

> Weep you no more, sad fountains;
> What need you flow so fast?
> Look how the snowy mountains
> Heaven's sun doth gently waste.
>> But my sun's heavenly eyes
>> View not your weeping,
>> That now lies sleeping
>> Softly, now softly lies
>>> Sleeping.

To tunes like these we are accustomed in poetry, we respond to the emotion even before the meaning of the words has been fully registered; Bridges communicates breathless delight with the lilt of

> When June is come, then all the day
> I'll sit with my love in the scented hay:
> And watch the sun-shot palaces high,
> That the white clouds build in the breezy sky.

Or Shelley strikes the note of a funeral bell with

> Death feeds on his mute voice and laughs at our despair.

But Donne rejoices and grieves in intricate patterns that work through the mind; he announces his pinnacle of joy in the measured tones of thought:

> True and false feares let us refraine,
> Let us love nobly, and live, and adde againe
> Yeares and yeares unto yeares, till we attaine
> To write threescore: this is the second of our raigne;[1]

[1] *The Anniversarie.*

and his elegiac music forces us to dwell on the meaning of
the words and the linking of thought with thought:

> 'Tis the yeares midnight, and it is the dayes,
> *Lucies*, who scarce seeven houres herself unmaskes,
> The Sunne is spent, and now his flasks
> Send forth light squibs, no constant rayes;
> The worlds whole sap is sunke:
> The generall balme th'hydroptique earth hath drunk,
> Whither, as to the beds-feet, life is shrunke,
> Dead and enterr'd; yet all these seeme to laugh,
> Compar'd with mee, who am their Epitaph.[1]

The monosyllables fall like hammerstrokes; then the
sound dies away in the short line

> The worlds whole sap is sunke:

and increases again in volume in the lines that follow with
the full tones of 'the generall balme th'hydroptique earth'
and the numbing thuds of sound: 'sunke', 'drunk',
'shrunke', 'dead'; lightened with an effect of sardonic
bitterness in the soft rhymes 'laugh: epitaph'; every twist
and turn in the sound pattern is a preparative for the despair
expressed in the central conceit of the poem:

> I, by loves limbecke, am the grave
> Of all, that's nothing.

Donne deliberately deprived himself of the hypnotic power
with which a regularly recurring beat plays upon the nerves.
He needed rhythm for another purpose; his rhythms arrest

---

[1] *A nocturnall upon S. Lucies day, Being the shortest day.* Mr Doniphan
Louthan argues persuasively that the occasion of this poem was the marriage
of Lucy Harrington to Edward Russell, third Earl of Bedford, Dec. 12th,
1594; the poem would be a lament for the loss of the beloved, but not by
her physical death. See *The Poetry of John Donne. An Explication.*
Bookman Associates, New York. The phrase 'as to the beds-feet' has been
found obscure. It was believed that the departing soul retreated, at the
moment of death, to the foot of the bed, cf. Bunyan, *The Life and Death
of Mr Badman*, '...and look, there stands the devil at my beds feet to
receive my soul when I die'.

and goad the reader, never quite fulfilling his expectations but forcing him to pause here and to rush on there, governing pace and emphasis so as to bring out the full force of the meaning. Traditional imagery and traditional rhythms are associated with traditional attitudes; but Donne wanted to express the complexity of his own moods, crude or subtle, harmonious or discordant. He had to find a more personal imagery and a more flexible rhythm. He made demands on his reader that no lyric poet had hitherto made. It is easy to miss his sound patterns through careless reading, because so much depends on the right distribution of pause and emphasis. His principal innovation was to make the cadences of speech the staple of his rhythm; contemporary dramatists had done this in blank verse, but no one had so far attempted it in lyrical poetry. It is this which makes the opening lines of his poems often so arresting:

> Now thou hast lov'd me one whole day,
> To morrow when thou leav'st, what wilt thou say?[1]

or

> He is starke mad, who ever sayes,
> That he hath beene in love an houre,[2]

or

> If yet I have not all thy love,
> Deare, I shall never have it all.[3]

Set in such different emotional keys, these opening lines are alike in their successful rendering of the accent of speech. It is speech of a peculiar kind, not the rhetorical speech of Dryden's verse, not the nimble give and take of dialogue, such as Pope gives in his *Epistle to Arbuthnot* nor yet the simple speech rhythms of Hardy at his best. It is a dramatic rhythm which gives the illusion of talk in a state of excitement:

> Oh doe not die, for I shall hate
> All women so, when thou art gone,[4] . . .

[1] *Woman's constancy.*
[2] *The broken heart.*
[3] *Lovers infiniteness.*
[4] *A Feaver.*

Nothing could be closer to the spoken word or more apparently inevitable. With the further elaboration of the thought that follows, the rhythm becomes more complicated:

> O wrangling schooles, that search what fire
>   Shall burne this world, had none the wit
> Unto this knowledge to aspire,
>   That this her feaver might be it?

> And yet shee cannot wast by this,
>   Nor long beare this torturing wrong,
> For much corruption needfull is
>   To fuell such a feaver long.

The inverted feet in the second stanza emphasize the words denoting pain; both the sound pattern and the sense demand slower reading:

> Nor lóng | beáre this | tórturing | wróng.

Constantly it will be found that reading aloud, by someone sensitive to the dramatic value of words, discovers a deliberate intention in Donne's irregularities:

> *Love*, any devill else but you,
> Would for a given Soule give something too.
> At Court your fellowes every day,
> Give th'art of Riming, Huntsmanship, or Play,
> For them which were their owne before;
> Onely I have nothing which gave more,
> But am, alas, by being lowly, lower.[1]

The general inharmoniousness reflects the discordant mood, and a clear and effective sound pattern emerges when the emphasis is thrown strongly on the important words, for instance on 'given' in line 2, on 'I' and 'gave' in line 6.

Donne's rhythm demands variety of pace. He has been called the most rapid of poets, and also the slowest. Both statements are true. A poem may begin slowly and presently hurry the reader into a rapidity that is almost breathless.

[1] *Loves exchange.*

> For every houre that thou wilt spare mee now,
>   I will allow,
> Usurious God of Love, twenty to thee,
> When with my browne, my gray haires equall bee;

So far a measured and dignified bargaining:

> Till then, Love, let my body raigne, and let
> Mee travell, sojourne, snatch, plot, have, forget,
> Resume my last yeares relict: thinke that yet
>   We'had never met.[1]

The pace increases through the successive monosyllables
'let'—'let', 'snatch, plot, have forget' down to the staccato
of the last short line. Equally hurried is the opening verse
of *The Canonization*:

> For Godsake hold your tongue, and let me love,
>   Or chide my palsie, or my gout,
> My five gray haires, or ruin'd fortune flout,
>   With wealth your state, your minde with Arts improve,
>   Take you a course, get you a place,
>   Observe his honour, or his grace,
>   Or the Kings reall, or his stamped face
>   Contemplate, what you will, approve,
>   So you will let me love.

And Donne continues to race through the catalogue of
advice to would-be carpers, finally slowing down to the
pomp of the last lines:

> And by these hymnes, all shall approve
> Us *Canoniz'd* for Love:
> And thus invoke us; You whom reverend love
>   Made one anothers hermitage;
> You, to whom love was peace, that now is rage;
>   Who did the whole worlds soule contract, and drove
>   Into the glasses of your eyes
>   (So made such mirrors, and such spies,
> That they did all to you epitomize,)
>   Countries, Townes, Courts: Beg from above
>   A patterne of your love!

Certain poems demand a slow and measured reading
throughout, for instance *The Dreame, A Valediction: Of*

----

[1] *Loves Usury.*

Weeping, and *The Anniversarie*, with the magnificent pomp of its opening stanza:

> All Kings, and all their favorites,
>   All glory of honors, beauties, wits,
> The Sun it selfe, which makes times, as they passe,
> Is elder by a yeare, now, then it was
> When thou and I first one another saw:
> All other things, to their destruction draw,
>   Only our love hath no decay;
> This, no to morrow hath, nor yesterday,
> Running it never runs from us away,
> But truly keepes his first, last, everlasting day,

through the slow intricacy of the central stanza and on to the restrained passion of the close. If the reading is anywhere hurried, much of the poem's richness is lost. *A nocturnall upon S. Lucies day*, already quoted, is equally slow and needs sensitive reading aloud to produce its full effect. That it must be read slowly is obvious; the difficulty here is to allow the pauses required by the sense, without losing the sound pattern, when the sense runs on from line to line. A similar difficulty is commonly experienced in reading blank verse aloud, and particularly the blank verse of Donne's contemporaries, Webster or Middleton. Too marked a pause or too little can equally well mar the rhythm. The same type of difficulty occurs in reading a poet who resembles Donne in some ways, Gerard Manley Hopkins. Hopkins, like Donne, governs the emphasis with great subtlety. He uses Donne's trick of breaking up the lines suddenly, indicating a pause or intake of breath by means of an exclamatory monosyllable:

But ah, but O thou terrible, why wouldst thou rude on me
Thy wring-world right foot rock? lay a lionlimb against me?
    scan
With darksome devouring eyes my bruiséd bones? and fan,
O in turns of tempest, me heaped there; me frantic to avoid
    thee and flee?[1]

[1] Gerard Manley Hopkins, *Carrion Comfort*.

46

Compare Donne's use of the monosyllable 'Oh':

> If rivall fooles taxe thee to'have lov'd a man,
> So foule, and course, as, Oh, I may seeme than.[1]

> I planted knowledge and life's tree in thee,
> Which Oh, shall strangers taste?[2]

> I, like an usurpt towne, to'another due,
> Labour to'admit you, but Oh, to no end,[3]

> She that, Oh, broke her faith, would soon breake thee.[4]

Hopkins is like Donne too in the interweaving and opposition between the pauses dictated by the meaning and those dictated by the pattern:

> O the mind, mind has mountains; cliffs of fall
> Frightful, sheer, no-man-fathomed. Hold them cheap
> May who ne'er hung there. Nor does long our small
> Durance deal with that steep or deep. Here! creep,
> Wretch, under a comfort serves in a whirlwind: all
> Life death does end and each day dies with sleep.[5]

Donne's basic metre is the iambic five foot line. Ben Jonson complained of his 'not keeping of accent'; sometimes he shifts the stress from the second to the first syllable of a foot, sometimes he introduces extra syllables, indicating that they should be slurred. For instance:

> Í, like | an ús|urpt tówne |, to'áno| ther dúe,
> Lábour | to'admít | you, bút | Óh, to | no énd,
> Réason | your více|roy in mée, | me shóuld | defénd,
> But ís | captív'd, | and próves | wéake or | untrúe.

Hopkins uses 'sprung rhythm' which he describes as follows: 'To speak shortly, it consists in scanning by accents or stresses alone, without any account of the number of

---

[1] *Elegie* v.   [2] *Elegie* vii.
[3] *Holy Sonnet* xiv.   [4] *A Jeat Ring Sent.*
[5] No 41, in Robert Bridges' edition, O.U.P.

syllables, so that a foot may be one strong syllable or it may be many light and one strong.'[1]

Both poets ring their changes on the rhythm of spoken English, their variations reflect the emotions of an impassioned speaker. Both poets are governed by metrical laws but both prefer a flexible system. Their patterns are dramatic, they appear to arise out of the needs of the moment rather than to be imposed beforehand.

None of Donne's immediate successors had his wide range of emotional experience, none needed his wide variety of rhythmical pattern. But his principal innovations were freely copied. The simplicity and seeming inevitability of phrase which is one of Herbert's most striking characteristics owes its origin to Donne who, it is sometimes forgotten, was as capable of simplicity as of subtlety. The derivation of Herbert's rhythms is best seen when Donne is remembered as the poet of such lines as

> All day, the same our postures were,
>   And wee said nothing, all the day.[2]
>
> What e'er she meant by'it, bury it with me,[3]
>
> That love is weake, where feare's as strong as hee;[4]

or

> Why should we rise, because 'tis light?
> Did we lie downe, because 'twas night?[5]

The moving tones of human speech, grown metrical in apparently inevitable response to the feeling that prompts it, is not the least of the gifts Donne bestowed on the poets who were influenced by him.

[1] *The Correspondence of Gerard Manley Hopkins and Richard Watson Dixon*, edited by Claud Colleer Abbott. Letter III.
[2] *The Extasie.*   [3] *The Funerall.*
[4] *The Dreame.*   [5] *Breake of Day.*

CHAPTER IV

GEORGE HERBERT, 1593–1633

Cannot thy love
Heighten a spirit to sound out thy praise
As well as any she?   GEORGE HERBERT

ERBERT'S mother, Magdalene Herbert, was the
addressee of several of Donne's poems and letters.
When she died he made for her a magnificent funeral
oration; he must often have visited that house which he
describes as 'a court in the conversation of the best' and
George Herbert must have been early acquainted with
manuscripts of his poetry. The influence of the elder poet
on the younger was strong and permanent. Herbert's
imagery, like Donne's, works through the mind rather than
the senses and the structure of his poems is logical. But, for
various reasons, his poetry is simpler than Donne's. The
range of his experience was narrower. Donne expresses
hate, disgust, jealousy, lust, love, reverence, security and
mistrust. He traverses every variety of mood, both as a
lover and as a worshipper; and at any given moment the
experiences he has already passed through are still present
to him. Each poem represents a complex state of mind and
a subtle adjustment of impulses. Herbert's narrower
experience not only limits his choice of subject-matter, but
simplifies the texture of his poems.

At an early age Herbert decided that the emotional peace
and satisfaction he sought was not to be found in the love
of women. He shut himself off from the whole field of
experience in which Donne's *Songs and Sonets* found their
origin. His mother was the only woman to whom he ever
addressed a poem. When he was only four years old his
father died and Magdalene Herbert was free to give all her

devotion and shaping influence to her children. She moved with little George to Oxford, where Edward was then studying, and remained there for four years, with both her sons under her eye, George working with tutors and Edward reading for his degree. Afterward she moved with George to London and he went as a day-boy to Westminster College. Not till 1609, the year in which he entered the university, did his mother marry again; so that, throughout his childhood and adolescence, and right up to the threshold of manhood, he had been closely and lovingly watched over by a mother who, as we know, was no ordinary woman. Izaak Walton speaks of her 'great and harmlesse wit, her cheerful gravity and obliging behaviour', but Donne, in his funeral sermon, draws a stronger portrait. He tells us of her 'inclination and conversation, naturally cheerful, and merry, and loving facetiousness, and sharpnesse of wit...', and, with impassioned eloquence, he tells of her generosity to the plague-stricken: 'of which, myself, who, at that time, had the favour to be admitted into that family, can, and must testify this, that when the late heavy visitation fell hotly upon this towne, when every doore was shut up, and, lest Death should enter into the house, every house was made a sepulchre of them that were in it, then, then, in that time of infection, diverse persons visited with that infection, had their releefe, and releefe applicable to that very infection, from this house.' And, finally, he tells us how 'In the doctrine, and discipline of that Church, in which God sealed her to himselfe in Baptisme, shee brought up her children, she assisted her family, she dedicated her soule to God in her life and surrendered it to him in her death; and in that forme of Common Prayer, which is ordained by that Church, and to which she accustomed herself, with her family, twice every day, she joined with that company, which was about her death bed'. We are left with the picture of a woman of quick intelligence, unusual courage, firmness of will and strong religious zeal, who coveted her son's devotion, not for herself, but for the Church. She had always intended George for the Church; soldiering was the family profession, but for this he had not the physique and he resigned himself, at first reluctantly, to an academic career which was to end in a country parsonage. For New Year's day 1610 he sent to his mother his first two poems. The theme of both was the inadequacy of earthly loves. In an accompanying letter he declared that he did not need the help of the muses 'to reprove the vanity of those many love poems that are daily writ, and consecrated to Venus; nor to bewail that so few are writ that look towards God and heaven. For my own part, my meaning (dear mother) is, in these sonnets, to declare my resolution to be, that my poor abilities in poetry, shall be all and ever consecrated to God's glory.' The sonnets show the influence of Donne; the first begins with a question, the second with a statement, each perfectly reproducing the accent of the spoken word:

> My God, where is that ancient heat towards thee,
> Wherewith whole showls of *Martyrs* once did burn,
>   Besides their other flames? Doth Poetry
> Wear *Venus* Livery? only serve her turn?
> Why are not *Sonnets* made of thee? and layes
>   Upon thine Altar burnt? Cannot thy love
>   Heighten a spirit to sound out thy praise
> As well as any she? Cannot thy *Dove*
> Out-strip their *Cupid* easily in flight?

The macabre jest about the flames is in the metaphysical tradition, as is the conceit with which the second sonnet closes:

> Open the bones, and you shall nothing find
>   In the best *face* but *filth*, when, Lord, in thee
>   The *beauty* lies in the *discovery*.

Herbert never wavered in his resolution to devote his poetic gifts exclusively to the service of God. In a poem called *Dulnesse*, we find him again drawing a parallel between his own theme and that of the love poet:

> The wanton lover in a curious strain
> > Can praise his fairest fair;
> And with quaint metaphors her curled hair
> > Curl o're again.
>
> Thou art my lovelinesse, my life, my light,
> > Beautie alone to me:
> Thy bloudy death and undeserv'd, makes thee
> > Pure red and white.

And the same conscious choice of the love of God as alternative to the love of women prompts *A Parodie*, in which Herbert follows the pattern of a song once thought to have been by Donne,

> Soules joy, now I am gone,
> > And you alone,
> > (Which cannot be,
> Since I must leave myselfe with thee,
> > And carry thee with me)
> > Yet when unto our eyes
> > > Absence denyes
> > > Each others sight,
> And makes to us a constant night,
> > When others change to light
> > > *O give no way to griefe,*
> > > *But let beliefe*
> > > > *Of mutuall love,*
> > > *This wonder to the vulgar prove*
> > > *Our Bodyes, not wee move.*[1]

For Herbert it is God, not an earthly lover, whose absence is inconceivable:

> Souls joy, when thou art gone,
> > And I alone,
> > > Which cannot be,
> Because thou dost abide with me,
> > And I depend on thee;

[1] Sir Herbert Grierson prints this among the poems attributed to Donne (Appendix B VIII, *Song*, probably by the Earl of Pembroke).

Herbert married Jane Danvers in 1629; he was thirty-six years old and in failing health. It was a childless though, we are told, a happy marriage. Herbert died four years later. A year after his marriage he accepted the living of Bemerton. The two events were not unconnected. Marriage was a carefully considered step in his consecration to God's service. In the prose treatise called *The Country Parson* we learn what he thought about a married priesthood:

The Country Parson considering that virginity is a higher state then Matrimony, and that the Ministry requires the best and highest things, is rather unmarryed, then marryed. But yet as the temper of his body may be, or as the temper of his Parish may be, where he may have occasion to converse with women, and that among suspicious men, . . . he is rather married then unmarried.

And of the choice of a wife he writes:

If he be married, the choyce of his wife was made rather by his eare, then by his eye; his judgement, not his affection found out a fit wife for him, whose humble, and liberall disposition he preferred before beauty, riches, or honour.[1]

Thus circumspectly, in strong contrast to the headlong impetuosity of John Donne, Herbert probably chose his own wife.

But it must not be supposed that Herbert was of a placid or equable temperament. Lord Herbert of Cherbury tells us in his autobiography that 'my brother George was not exempt from passion and choler (being infirmities to which all our race is subject)'. And Herbert, in his autobiographical poems *Affliction*, speaks of his 'fierce and sudden' youth; the poems often describe his servitude to God as a bondage against which he vainly rebels.

> I struck the board, and cry'd, No more.
>   I will abroad.
>   What? shall I ever sigh and pine?
> My lines and life are free; free as the rode,
>   Loose as the winde, as large as store.
>   Shall I be still in suit?

[1] *A Priest to the Temple or The Country Parson his Character etc.* Chap. IX.

Have I no harvest but a thorn
To let me bloud, and not restore
What I have lost with cordiall fruit?
Sure there was wine
Before my sighs did drie it: there was corn
Before my tears did drown it.
Is the yeare onely lost to me?
Have I no bayes to crown it?
No flowers, no garlands gay? all blasted?
All wasted?

The Collar, which is this poem's title, is an emblem of servitude. The poem moves through rebellion against his Master to the sudden recognition that the freedom he is claiming is freedom from God's love:

But as I rav'd and grew more fierce and wilde
At every word,
Me thoughts I heard one calling, *Child!*
And I reply'd, *My Lord.*

His poetry is not the record of quiet saintliness, but of continual wrestling and continual submission; the collar is not easily worn:

I know the wayes of Pleasure, the sweet strains,
The lullings and the relishes of it;
The propositions of hot bloud and brains;
What mirth and musick mean; what love and wit
Have done these twentie hundred yeares, and more:
I know the projects of unbridled store:
My stuffe is flesh, not brasse; my senses live,
And grumble oft, that they have more in me
Then he that curbs them, being but one to five:
Yet I love thee.[1]

No human love competed with the love of God for Herbert; but the fuller life of worldly intercourse and the sweets of ambition allured him: he complains in *Affliction* (1):

Whereas my birth and spirit rather took
The way that takes the town;
Thou didst betray me to a lingring book,
And wrap me in a gown.

[1] *The Pearl. Matthew* xiii. 45.

Charles Cotton speaks of him as

> He whose education
> Manners and parts, by high applauses blown,
> Was deeply tainted by Ambition,
> And fitted for a court,...[1]

which is in keeping with Herbert's confession in *Afflic-tion* (1), that:

> Thou often didst with Academick praise
> Melt and dissolve my rage.

and in *The Country Parson* he describes ambition as one of the commonest and most insidious temptations with which men of his calling can be afflicted:

> Ambition, or untimely desire of promotion to an higher state or place, under colour of accommodation or necessary provision, is a common temptation to men of any eminency....

This was the temptation that Herbert resisted, though not without rebellion and remonstrance:

> Were it not better to bestow
> Some place and power on me?
> Then should thy praises with me grow,
> And share in my degree.

he urges in *Submission*,

> But when I thus dispute and grieve,
> I do resume my sight,
> And pilfring what I once did give,
> Disseize thee of thy right.

To reject God, for Herbert, would be to prefer the prizes and praises of the world to the act of loving, for God has no rival in his heart. That is why he suffers so acutely under the ebb and flow of his own zeal:

> How should I praise thee, Lord! how should my rymes
> Gladly engrave thy love in steel,
> If what my soul doth feel sometimes,
> My soul might ever feel![2]

[1] Quoted by George Herbert Palmer in his edition of *The English Works of George Herbert*. Houghton Mifflin & Co. 3 vols, 1905; revised, 1907; reissued, 1915. [2] *The Temper* (1).

No theme occurs more frequently, or is more poignantly expressed, than this distress at the dying away of emotion:

> Whither away delight?
> Thou cam'st but now; wilt thou so soon depart,
>   And give me up to night?[1]

His over-mastering desire is to be allowed to love God; the need expressed in the passionate paradox with which *Affliction* (I) closes. He has toyed with the thought of seeking some other service and suddenly he turns back to his first and only love with the despairing cry:

> Ah my deare God! though I am clean forgot,
> Let me not love thee, if I love thee not.

Herbert's poetry is the expression of an ardent temperament with a single emotional outlet.

With the exception of a few didactic poems interpreting the doctrine or ritual of the Church, all his poetry is spiritual autobiography. The devotional poet, perhaps even more than the love poet, is exposed to the danger of confiding in his public instead of writing poems. His problem is to build a structure that will stand alone, independently of either the reader's or the poet's private concerns. It is here that the 'Donne tradition' is salutary. Within that tradition the structure of a poem is normally dialectic. Herbert states his premises with precision, usually by means of an image, in the tone of a prose argument. The reader is never be-fogged; the words represent clear-cut ideas which are the medium through which the poet's emotion is conveyed as well as, often, the cause of that emotion. Herbert knows and states what he thinks, as well as what he feels, about, for example, death and immortality or the relation between God and the soul. This does not mean that his poems are arguments designed to persuade the reader. Herbert takes the reader's intellectual assent for granted. He writes for his fellow-Christian. The substance of each poem is

---

[1] *The Glimpse.*

emotional, but the emotion is rooted in thought. As the reader absorbs the poem he becomes aware of that fusion between thought and feeling which constitutes the poet's belief. Suspension of his own irrelevant incredulities is easier than it is with poetry whose intellectual structure is less self-sufficient. A comparison will make the difference clearer. Herbert in a poem called *Death* and Tennyson in stanza CXXIX of *In Memoriam*, each assert a belief in immortality. Tennyson addresses the spirit of his dead friend:

> Thy voice is on the rolling air;
>   I hear thee where the waters run;
>   Thou standest in the rising sun,
> And in the setting thou art fair.
>
> What art thou then? I cannot guess;
>   But tho' I seem in star and flower
>   To feel thee some diffusive power,
> I do not therefore love thee less:
>
> My love involves the love before;
>   My love is vaster passion now;
>   Tho' mix'd with God and Nature thou,
> I seem to love thee more and more.
>
> Far off thou art, but ever nigh;
>   I have thee still, and I rejoice;
>   I prosper, circled with thy voice;
> I shall not lose thee tho' I die.

A statement in the first stanza is followed in the second by a question to which no answer is forthcoming:

> What art thou then? I cannot guess;

and in the third and fourth stanzas there are further statements again, but they are intentionally vague. The words 'I seem' dominate the stanza, the total impression left with the reader is that Tennyson perhaps knew what he felt, but certainly not what he thought. Herbert's poem *Death* is based on the premise that the death of Christ is the pledge of our resurrection; that he assumes this is made plain in the poem by the juxtaposition of two contrasted pictures representing the pre-Christian and the Christian view of death:

> Death, thou wast once an uncouth hideous thing,
>> Nothing but bones,
>> The sad effect of sadder grones:
> Thy mouth was open, but thou couldst not sing.
>
> For we consider'd thee as at some six
>> Or ten yeares hence,
>> After the losse of life and sense,
> Flesh being turn'd to dust, and bones to sticks.
>
> We lookt on this side of thee, shooting short;
>> Where we did finde
>> The shells of fledge souls left behinde,
> Dry dust, which sheds no tears, but may extort.
>
> But since our Saviours death did put some bloud
>> Into thy face;
>> Thou art grown fair and full of grace,
> Much in request, much sought for as a good.
>
> For we do now behold thee gay and glad,
>> As at dooms-day;
>> When souls shall wear their new aray,
> And all thy bones with beautie shall be clad.
>
> Therefore we can go die as sleep, and trust
>> Half that we have
>> Unto an honest faithfull grave;
> Making our pillows either down, or dust.

The plot of the poem is clear and simple, three stanzas to describe death as it seemed before the resurrection, culminating in the lucid and lovely image of bodies that were but

> The shells of fledge souls left behinde,

which (with its suggestion of spring and birth) leads on to three stanzas describing death as it seems since the resurrection. The concrete imagery builds up two clearly contrasted pictures, each impregnated with its appropriate feeling, the horror of death the skeleton

> Thy mouth was open, but thou couldst not sing.

58

and the peace of death

> As at dooms-day;
> When souls shall wear their new aray,
> And all thy bones with beautie shall be clad.

A modern reader may be in closer sympathy with Tenny-son's indecision, but his stanza remains unsatisfactory as poetry, because he does not say what he means, nor quite mean what he says. Herbert, like Donne, was capable of clear thought in conjunction with vehement feeling. The two kinds of activity abetted each other, so that the logical plotting of a lyric suited his genius. But he modified Donne's style in other respects. His experiences were less complex, less varied, so that he could convey them more simply. He used words more widely current and more often selected his illustrations from every day life. In two poems called *Jordan*, Herbert describes his stylistic aims, setting them out in conscious distinction both from the elaborateness of the Petrarchists and from the intellectual subtlety of Donne:

> Is it no verse, except enchanted groves
> And sudden arbours shadow course-spunne lines?
> Must purling streams refresh a lovers loves?
> Must all be vail'd, while he that reades, divines,
>   Catching the sense at two removes?
>
> Shepherds are honest people; let them sing:
> Riddle who list, for me, and pull for Prime:
> I envie no mans nightingale or spring;
> Nor let them punish me with loss of rime,
>   Who plainly say, *My God, My King*.[1]

Herbert will not have pastoral affectations, neither will he have the intellectual curiosities of Donne.

> When first my lines of heav'nly joyes made mention,
> Such was their lustre, they did so excell,

---

[1] *Jordan* (1). F. E. Hutchinson in his invaluable edition *The Works of George Herbert* (Clarendon Press, 1941) explains 'pull for Prime'; it refers to the card game primero in which the player draws for a card or cards which will make him *prime*.

That I sought out quaint words, and trim invention;
My thoughts began to burnish, sprout, and swell,
Curling with metaphors a plain intention,
Decking the sense, as if it were to sell.

Thousands of notions in my brain did runne,
Off'ring their service, if I were not sped:
I often blotted what I had begunne;
This was not quick enough, and that was dead.
Nothing could seem too rich to clothe the sunne,
Much lesse those joyes which trample on his head.

As flames do work and winde, when they ascend,
So I did weave my self into the sense.
But while I bustled, I might heare a friend
Whisper, *How wide is all this long pretence!*
There is in love a sweetnesse readie penn'd:
Copie out onely that, and save expense.[1]

The two poems not only describe the kind of simplicity
Herbert intends, they also illustrate the simplicity he
achieves. It is the result of concrete imagery, familiar
diction and a sound pattern close to the rhythm of speech.
He chooses words that recall the affairs of every day. His
lines are 'course-spunne' and his imagery of the market
place. He creates for us, in the second poem, the picture
of a bustling salesman, fidgeting about his wares, 'decking
the sense, as if it were to sell', until he is advised to 'save
expense'. This is the kind of image he always prefers, an
image which associates his experience with the daily traffic
of men of affairs or with ordinary household business.
When, in *Church-lock and key*, he wants to describe his
flagging zeal, he likens himself to a cold man impatiently
bullying an insufficient fire:

But as cold hands are angrie with the fire,
        And mend it still;
So I do lay the want of my desire,
Not on my sinnes, or coldnesse, but thy will.

[1] *Jordan* (ii).

In *Confession* grief tortures a man as a carpenter tortures wood or an illness the body:

> No scrue, no piercer can
> Into a piece of timber work and winde,
> As Gods afflictions into man,
> When he a torture hath design'd.
> They are too subtill for the sub'tllest hearts;
> And fall, like rheumes, upon the tendrest parts.

He gains his effects from the short, strong, familiar words of daily usage:

> My throat, my soul is hoarse;
> My heart is wither'd like a ground
> Which thou dost curse.
> My thoughts turn round,
> And make me giddie; Lord, I fall,
> Yet call.[1]

Herbert often invented rhyme schemes or metrical patterns to illustrate the experience conveyed in the poem. In *Longing*, for instance, each stanza comes to rest in a two-foot line, which reflects the moment of exhaustion after stress:

> Look on my sorrows round!
> Mark well my furnace! O what flames,
> What heats abound!
> What griefs, what shames!
> Consider, Lord; Lord, bow thine eare,
> And heare!

The strong contrasts of crescendo and diminuendo are a favourite device with him. This and other emblematic uses of metre are effective for Herbert because he recreates regular patterns of feeling. Despite his use of logic, his poems rarely progress (as Donne's do) to an unforeseen conclusion. When they seem to do that (as in *The Collar*) the surprise is reserved for the last lines. The steps towards the resolution of an emotional problem, in Herbert's poems, are as similar to one another as are the stanza-forms that

---

[1] *Longing.*

communicate them. They advance, retreat, tread firmly, haltingly, or whatever it may be, in regular sequences. In *Deniall* Herbert invents a metre and rhyme scheme to reflect the broken relationship between God and the soul:

> When my devotions could not pierce
> Thy silent eares;
> Then was my heart broken, as was my verse:
> My breast was full of fears
> And disorder:

Each stanza ends with a short unrhymed line until the last, where the rhyme is completed to suggest the renewed harmonious relation with God that the poet desires.

> O cheer and tune my heartlesse breast,
> Deferre no time;
> That so thy favours granting my request,
> They and my minde may chime,
> And mend my ryme.[1]

Poets of more complex moods cannot deal so simply with the problem of relating sound to sense, their pattern cannot be predetermined with the same completeness. But what Herbert had to say was usually simple and the kind of device he invented was often admirable for his purpose. At times he went so far as to arrange a pattern for the eye as well as for the ear; in *The Altar* and in *Easter-wings* the subject is represented by the shape of the print upon the page.

It is a naïve device but adequate to the simple mood in which it was conceived. The effect of *Easter-wings* is less jejune than is sometimes supposed, for Herbert was sufficiently master of his instrument to make a double use of the pattern. The shape of the wings on the page may have meant more when Emblem Books were popular,[2]

---

[1] *Deniall.*
[2] See the chapter on George Herbert in *English Emblem Books* by Rosemary Freeman. London, 1948.

the diminuendo and crescendo that bring it about are expressive both of the rise and fall of the lark's song and flight (Herbert's image) and also of the fall of man and his resurrection in Christ (the subject that the image represents).

Lord, who createdst man in wealth and store,
Though foolishly he lost the same,
Decaying more and more,
Till he became
Most poore:
With thee
O let me rise
As larks, harmoniously,
And sing this day thy victories:
Then shall the fall further the flight in me.

My tender age in sorrow did beginne:
And still with sicknesses and shame
Thou didst so punish sinne,
That I became
Most thinne.
With thee
Let me combine
And feel this day thy victorie:
For, if I imp my wing on thine,
Affliction shall advance the flight in me.[1]

Herbert's poetry, despite his aristocratic birth and breeding and his considerable learning, leaves the impression of an unsophisticated mind. In certain ways the appeal of his verse is similar to the appeal of John Bunyan's prose. Like Bunyan, though for other reasons, he drew his language and imagery from daily affairs or from his religion. To understand him demands no culture that is not shared by all his co-religionists, and by the many more who are acquainted with the Bible and the teaching of the English church. But besides its simplicity in this sense, Herbert's poetry, like Bunyan's prose, exhibits certain childlike qualities of mind—the playfulness of some of his metrical effects is a case in point; a trick, for instance, like that of

[1] *imp my wing*: to imp, in falconry, is 'to engraft feathers in a damaged wing, so as to restore and improve the powers of flight' (O.E.D.) [quoted from F. E. Hutchinson, *ed. cit.*].

Trinitie Sunday in which three three-lined stanzas with triple rhymes represent the subject:

> Lord, who hast form'd me out of mud,
>   And hast redeem'd me through thy bloud,
>   And sanctifi'd me to do good;
>
> Purge all my sinnes done heretofore:
>   For I confesse my heavie score,
>   And I will strive to sinne no more.
>
> Enrich my heart, mouth, hands in me,
>   With faith, with hope, with charitie;
>   That I may runne, rise, rest with thee.

Such devices convey a child-like quality of mind, native to Herbert perhaps, or else acquired in obedience to the injunction 'except ye become as one of these little ones'. Patterns akin to the acrostic appealed to Herbert, he liked word games. In the poem *Paradise* for instance, cutting off the initial letter of the rhyme word represents God pruning his tree:

> I blesse thee, Lord, because I GROW
>   Among thy trees, which in a ROW
>   To thee both fruit and order OW,

and so on for five stanzas. Such playful effects as these, though exceptional in Herbert's work, indicate a fundamental difference between his mind and Donne's which accounts for other modifications he made in the metaphysical style.

Herbert profited from every aspect of Donne's style, but he always adapted it to his own temperament. He simplified the inner logical pattern, following as a rule a single train of argument; he changed the metrical pattern into something less flexible, though still studying to relate sound to sense; he narrowed the range of diction and imagery, while preserving their actuality. Similarly he adapted Donne's manner of accenting the line so as to reproduce the tone of the spoken word:

> I, like an usurp'd towne, to'another due,
> Labour to'admit you, but Oh, to no end,

writes Donne. This is the rhythm of speech, but only such as men speak under the stress of excitement. There is a suggestion of breathlessness, when we read the line we pant with the effort it describes. This was seldom the effect Herbert required, he preferred the tone of men exchanging news in the market place:

> Having been tenant long to a rich Lord,
> Not thriving, I resolved to be bold,[1]

It is on this level that Herbert's poems open, our attention is held, but our expectation is low pitched:

> My God, I heard this day,
> That none doth build a stately habitation
> But he that means to dwell therein.[2]

The relation between such an accent and the openings of Donne's poems is clear; Herbert like his master avoids the poetical, the words seem to fall into the natural prose order and to conform without effort to the metrical mould. But the climate of emotion is different:

> For Godsake hold your tongue and let me love!

writes Donne, or

> What if this present were the worlds last night?

No poet can afford to start at such a pitch unless he can sustain it or increase the tension. Herbert must start in low tones if we are to get the full impact of his climax, which consists often in a subtle change of feeling or attitude. His most characteristic gift is the power of controlling the movement of feeling in his poems. The emotional pattern is managed with exquisite tact. The attitudes he handles are subtle and delicate, over emphasis or emphasis in the wrong place, over haste or too much delay, would destroy their effect; but in such matters Herbert is a master. The opening lines of his poems are usually quiet, they place the reader at

[1] *Redemption.*　　　　[2] *Man.*

the heart of the subject just as Donne does, but, unlike Donne, Herbert maintains a demeanour of calm and restraint, and this is so even when, like Donne, he opens with an exclamation or question:

> Oh that I could a sinne once see![1]

> It cannot be. Where is that mightie joy
>   Which just now took up all my heart?[2]

> Oh, what a thing is man! How farre from power,
>   From setled peace and rest![3]

The mood is collected, it is the preparation for a discussion of the theme. A similar difference is noticeable between the closing lines of Herbert's poems and those of Donne or of Hopkins. Herbert constantly achieves his effect by relaxing the tension at the end of a poem. The struggle is over and all is peace. *The Thanksgiving*, for instance, is a discussion with God, in which the poet tries to offer an equivalent for all that has been given:

> If thou shalt give me wit, it shall appeare,
>   If thou hast giv'n it me, 'tis here.
> Nay, I will read thy book, and never move
>   Till I have found therein thy love,
> Thy art of love, which I'le turn back on thee:
>   O my deare Saviour, Victorie!

and then the poet falters and the culminating point of the poem suggests a lowering of the voice almost to a whisper:

> Then for thy passion—I will do for that—
>   Alas, my God, I know not what.

Such a dying away in the last line is Herbert's way of suggesting to his reader that the resources of language have been overpast, what remains to be said can only be stated with the utmost simplicity, as in the last line of *Dialogue* when he has enumerated and attempted to compete with all the sufferings of the Saviour:

> Ah no more: Thou break'st my heart,

[1] *Sinne* (II).   [2] *The Temper* (II).   [3] *Giddinesse.*

or the last line of *Miserie* in which he has described the folly and wickedness of man and ends with

> My God, I mean myself.

The first two words of the line are not an exclamation but a vocative; it is in an entirely different key from the last line of Hopkins' *Carrion Comfort*:

> That night, that year
> Of now done darkness I wretch lay wrestling with (my God!)
> my God.

If Hopkins had written the last line of Herbert's *Miserie* (if the fantasy may be allowed) it would have been an exclamation of agonized discovery:

> (My God!)—I mean myself,

instead of as at present a quiet, humiliated recognition of the fact. In poem no. 45 (in Robert Bridges' edition) Hopkins considers the subject of Herbert's poem *Miserie*, the abject nature of mankind and therefore of himself: he closes his poem when the horror is at its height:

> I am gall, I am heartburn. God's most deep decree
> Bitter would have me taste: my taste was me;
> Bones built in me, flesh filled, blood brimmed the curse,
>   Selfyeast of spirit a dull dough sours. I see
> The lost are like this, and their scourge to be
> As I am mine, their swetting selves; but worse.

Hopkins' sonnets are a crescendo of emotion, the strongest expression is reserved for the last line. Herbert, on the contrary, comes to rest on a note of quiet acceptance, some sentence that would be mere matter of fact, were it not for what has preceded. Yet the influence of Donne is conceivably present in either case; so differently can poets of different temperament make use of a common tradition. The best known and perhaps the most perfect of Herbert's poems, *Love* (III), will illustrate the measure of that difference.

> Love bade me welcome: yet my soul drew back,
> > Guiltie of dust and sinne.
> But quick-ey'd Love, observing me grow slack
> > From my first entrance in,
> Drew nearer to me, sweetly questioning,
> > If I lack'd any thing.
>
> A guest, I answer'd, worthy to be here:
> > Love said, You shall be he.
> I the unkinde, ungratefull? Ah my deare,
> > I cannot look on thee.
> Love took my hand, and smiling did reply,
> > Who made the eyes but I?
>
> Truth Lord, but I have marr'd them: let my shame
> > Go where it doth deserve.
> And know you not, sayes Love, who bore the blame?
> > My deare, then I will serve.
> You must sit down, sayes Love, and taste my meat:
> > So I did sit and eat.

No poem better represents the way in which Herbert assimilated and modified Donne's style. As so often with Donne, the plot of the poem is an argument, in this case a simple discussion between two persons. The relation between the soul and God is symbolized by a commonplace human situation, a travel-worn and shamefaced guest receiving hospitality. But Herbert, unlike Donne, develops his single situation at leisure and governs his reader's emotion almost entirely by his management of the tension. Starting at a low pitch he reaches the emotional climax in the middle of the poem:

> I the unkinde, ungratefull? Ah my deare,
> > I cannot look on thee.

and can then afford to relax gradually, completing his picture, but without emphasis; when the end is reached the emotion has become so poignant that the simple monosyllables in their prose order,

> So I did sit and eat.

convey more than the most impassioned rhetoric. All the feeling, that Herbert has so gradually and unostentatiously accumulated, rests upon the phrase. A graph might be made of the emotional plan of the poem in the shape of a pyramid; the two statements, 'Love bade me welcome; yet my soul drew back', and 'so I did sit and eat.' are the bases upon which it rests; at the apex is the cry of self-disgust.

When he settled in the parsonage at Bemerton, Herbert did not cease to be the exquisite courtier whom Walton so vividly describes. The same qualities of mind and temper found their outlet in poetry. In its sensitive modulations of tone we discern the master of social behaviour of whom Walton wrote that: 'if during his lifetime he expressed any error, it was, that he kept himself at too great a distance with all his inferiors; and his clothes seemed to prove that he put too great a value on his parts and parentage'; and again, 'the love of a court conversation, mixed with a laudable ambition to be something more than he was, drew him often to attend the king wheresoever the court was...he enjoyed his genteel humour for clothes, and court-like company, and seldom looked towards Cambridge unless the king were there, but then he never failed'. The element of vanity in such a temperament, or of social snobbery he overcame (witness the anecdotes at the end of Walton's life as well as the evidence of the poetry itself);[1] but the picture

[1] Walton tells us that Herbert went from time to time to Salisbury, to hear the Cathedral music and to 'sing and play his part at an appointed private music-meeting'. While walking to Salisbury on one such occasion, 'he saw a poor man with a poorer horse, that was fallen under his load: they were both in distress, and needed present help; which Mr Herbert perceiving, put off his canonical coat, and helped the poor man to unload, and after to load, his horse. The poor man blessed him for it, and he blessed the poor man; and was so like the Good Samaritan, that he gave him money to refresh both himself and his horse; and told him, "that if he loved himself he should be merciful to his beast". Thus he left the poor man: and at his coming to his musical friends at Salisbury, they began to wonder that Mr George Herbert, which used to be so trim and clean, came into that company so soiled and discomposed: but he told them the occasion. And when one of the company told him "He had disparaged himself by so dirty an employment," his answer was, "That the thought of what he had done would prove music to him at midnight; and that the omission of it would have upbraided and made discord in his conscience, whensoever he should

sorts well with some of the most characteristic qualities of the poems. His perfect tact and delicate rendering of the changes of feeling or attitude, and above all his easy command of the right tone, without bluster, without self-consciousness: all this may well owe something to his breeding and his early intercourse.

pass by that place: for if I be bound to pray for all that be in distress, I am sure that I am bound, so far as it is in my power, to practise what I pray for. And though I do not wish for the like occasion every day, yet let me tell you, I would not willingly pass one day of my life without comforting a sad soul, or showing mercy; and I praise God for this occasion. And now let us tune our instruments."'

CHAPTER V

HENRY VAUGHAN, 1622–1695

> The third requisite in our poet is imitation, to be able to
> convert the riches or substance of another poet to his own
> use.
>   BEN JONSON

VAUGHAN was fascinated by the phrases of other
poets. This is not unusual in a young poet; but the
habit of borrowing continued with Vaughan to the
end. At first his borrowings strike no roots, they are picked
blossoms that have caught his fancy, later they are young
shoots that bloom anew in his poems. In his two collections
of secular poems, *Poems, with the Tenth Satire of Juvenal
Englished* (1646) and *Olor Iscanus* (1651), the most obvious
debts are to Donne and Habington, though he is attracted
also by the Elizabethan use of mythological names and their
Petrarchan attitude to the mistress. He seldom strikes a
personal note; one suspects he is not sure of what he wants
to say. His poems seem to fall apart, an elaborate image is
followed by a lame conclusion. He is more interested in
poetry than in his poem. In *Silex Scintillans* (1650),
Herbert's influence is predominant. He rehandles Herbert's
themes, borrows his phrases, copies his metrical effects,
repeats his titles and yet now the poem is his own. Whatever he takes from Herbert he transmutes because his way
of apprehending is different. The influence of Herbert's
teaching, and probably other influences as well,[1] operated
a 'conversion' in Vaughan and he became a religious poet;
but his religious experience was unlike Donne's or Herbert's
and required for its expression different imagery and
different rhythms.

[1] Miss Elizabeth Holmes, in *Henry Vaughan and the Hermetic Philosophy*
(Oxford, 1932), discusses the nature of these influences.

Vaughan's indebtedness in his early volumes needs no elaborating. Mr L. C. Martin, in his excellent edition (Clarendon Press, 1914), notes the various parallels. The fact that Vaughan borrows phrases, images or whole lines from his contemporaries is unimportant; it was the custom of the time. Donne's phrases are remodelled or even merely repeated in the poems of Carew, of Habington, of Suckling, of Godolphin and it is not surprising that Vaughan too made use of them, sometimes taking them direct from Donne himself, sometimes preferring the version of an imitator. But there are two peculiarities in these early poems. The first is that Vaughan never appears to be interested in his subject. He plays lovingly with an image and delays its application which is finally huddled into a last stanza. The other is that he prefers to draw his images from the countryside even when his model was Donne, who seldom looked in that direction. The result is often that his own experience, which finds an outlet in the image, has no inevitable connection with the situation to which he applies it with a logic more painstaking than convincing.

To Amoret, *of the difference 'twixt him, and other*
Lovers, and what true Love is.

Marke, when the Evenings cooler wings
　　Fanne the afflicted ayre, how the faint Sunne,
　　　　Leaving undone,
　　　　What he begunne,
Those spurious flames suckt up from slime, and earth
　　　　To their first, low birth,
　　　　Resignes, and brings.

They shoot their tinsill beams, and vanities,
　　Thredding with those false fires their way;
　　　　But as you stay
　　　　And see them stray,
You loose the flaming track, and subt'ly they
　　　　Languish away,
　　　　And cheate your Eyes.

Just so base, Sublunarie Lovers hearts
    Fed on loose prophane desires,
        May for an Eye,
        Or face comply:
But those removed, they will as soone depart,
        And shew their Art
        And painted fires.

Whilst I by pow'rfull Love, so much refin'd
    That my absent soule the same is
        Carelesse to misse,
        A glaunce, or kisse,
Can with those Elements of lust and sence,
        Freely dispence,
        And court the mind.

Thus to the North the Loadstones move,
    And thus to them th'enamour'd steel aspires:
        Thus, *Amoret*,
        I doe affect;
And thus by winged beames, and mutuall fire,
        Spirits and Stars conspire,
        And this is L O V E.

In the first two stanzas he is describing an effect of the
evening light which he himself has noted: he has no literary
model, he is interested, and he dwells on more detail than
he can make use of for his parallel. There is no convincing
relation between the behaviour of light at sunset and of
'base, Sublunarie Lovers hearts'; they remain two separate
observations arbitrarily linked together. He fares no better
in the last stanza, into which he crowds two more images,
the already hackneyed loadstone, and the image beloved by
Donne of the stars in their spheres governed by an 'intelligence' or spirit.[1] The total impression left by Vaughan's
poem is that the metaphysical conceit was, at this time, a
fashion he accepted rather than the outcome of his own
habit of mind. He had not, like Donne, the kind of mind
that is immediately aware of logical situations recurring in

[1] Cf. *The Extasie* and *Aire and Angels*. The scholastic belief which the
image assumes is explained in Professor Grierson's notes to these poems

diverse kinds of experience; nor had he as yet, what he was
to discover later, a conception of the universe as a whole,
which would lead him to perceive a relation between its
various parts. There are signs in these early poems of the
direction in which Vaughan would look for such a conception. His poetry becomes sensitive and individual when
it describes nature, as it does nowhere else. He dwells with
loving particularity on scenes he has noted, and especially
on changes of light. A modern reader, wise after the event,
can recognize the poet of *The Dawning*, *The Morning-
watch*, *Midnight*, *The Search* and the many more in which
sunrise, sunset and starlight are significant, when he reads
such a poem as *To Amoret gone from Him* with its sensitive,
although half fanciful, description of the way in which the
life fades out of a country scene at sunset:

> How the Spring
> That smil'd, and curl'd about his beames,
> Whilst he was here, now check'd her streames:
> The wanton Eddies of her face
> Were taught lesse noise, and smoother grace;
> And in a slow, sad channell went,
> Whisp'ring the banks their discontent:
> The carelesse ranks of flowers that spread
> Their perfum'd bosomes to his head,
> And with an open, free Embrace,
> Did entertaine his beamy face;
> Like absent friends point to the West,
> And on that weake reflection feast.

His secular poems, lacking as they do any individual outlook, only come to life when they reflect his responsiveness
to the world about him. He looks even at nature partly
through the eyes of other poets, but his own awareness and
interest percolate through their phrases and fancies, even
when he is writing complimentary verses, for instance: *To
the best, and most accomplish'd Couple—*

> Fresh as the *houres* may all your pleasures be,
> And healthfull as *Eternitie*!

> Sweet as the flowres *first breath*, and Close
> As th'*unseen spreadings* of the Rose,
> When he unfolds his Curtained head,
> And makes his bosome the *Suns bed*,

which, with its feeling for the secret, luxurious beauty of the rose, recalls Blake's *Sick Rose*, and Shelley's rose in *The Sensitive Plant*

> Which unveiled the depth of her glowing breast
> Till, fold after fold, to the fainting air
> The soul of her beauty and love lay bare.

What was needed to make Vaughan a poet who stands out from the contemporary galaxy of good versifiers, was some central experience to which to relate his awareness of nature. His poems became entities when he recognized the phenomena of nature as relevant to his interpretation of the world.

The main importance of Herbert's influence is that it helped him to this end. Vaughan's preface to the second edition of *Silex Scintillans* (1655) suggests that, whatever influences combined to make him a religious *man*, Herbert was largely instrumental in making him a religious *poet*. Vaughan here dissociates himself from 'those ingenious persons, which in the late notion are termed *Wits*', namely, those poets whom in his first two volumes he had, almost slavishly, imitated 'and here' he adds 'because I would prevent a just *censure* by my free *confession*, I must remember, that I my self have, for many years together, languished of this very *sickness*; and it is no long time since I have recovered. But (blessed be God for it!) I have by his saving assistance suppress my *greatest follies*, and those which escaped from me, are (I think) as innoxious, as most of that *vein* use to be; besides, they are interlin'd with many virtuous, and some pious mixtures.' Something had happened to make him turn away with contempt from the amorous verse he had so lately practised and he now claimed a new allegiance to 'that blessed man *Mr George Herbert*, whose holy *life* and *verse* gained many pious

Converts (of whom I am the least) and gave the first check to a most flourishing and admired wit of his time'.

Under Herbert's influence Vaughan discovered what he really wanted to say. He was passionately concerned, like Herbert himself, with the relation between God and the individual soul, and this concern increased and gave significance to his observations in the external world. When Vaughan began to explore his religious belief he found that it centred in his conception of nature. From being merely an ornament or an illustration his perceptiveness became the core of his poetry. Vaughan emerged from his contact with Herbert a metaphysical poet, not because Herbert was a metaphysical poet and he an imitative one, but because he now achieved a sense of direction and became capable of correlating his experiences. When he constructed his poems to *Amoret* on the metaphysical plan, he was only an imitator. His arguments were ingenious elaborations of 'occult resemblances'. But in true metaphysical poetry the intellectual parallel, or the recondite image, expresses awareness of a world in which the separate and apparently unrelated parts strangely echo one another. They are suddenly seen in the poetry as facets of a single whole. So it is when Donne cries out to his weeping mistress:

> O more than Moone,
> Draw not up seas to drowne me in thy spheare,

or when, in *The Extasie*, he describes the relation between the self and the body:

> Wee are
> The intelligences, they the spheare.
> We owe them thankes, because they thus,
> Did us, to us, at first convay,
> Yeelded their forces, sense, to us,
> Nor are drosse to us, but allay.

Successful metaphysical imagery demands and repays close scrutiny. The meaning of the image tends to expand as we

contemplate it, for instance in Donne's image of the moon
his mistress is 'more than Moone' because she is more fair,
more dear; because she draws the poet to her as the moon
the tides; because she draws up tears as the moon will draw
up the seas on which he is about to voyage; and her tears
are salt like the seas and like the seas they may destroy him.
All this and more is compressed within the image. In false
metaphysical poetry the relation contemplated depends
upon a one-sided and superficial resemblance. Of such a
kind is the predominant difference between Vaughan's
secular poetry and *Silex Scintillans*. He contemplates the
same things, sunset and starlight, birds and flowers; but,
whereas before he looked round for a subject they could
adorn and contented himself with a partial relevance, they
now appear in the poetry as the terms in which he is thinking;
their relation to the subject is therefore intricate and rich.
The lingering light of evening, for instance, so laboriously
linked with the thought of his absent mistress in *To Amoret
gone from him*, is now identified with the effect upon his
mind of the memory of the dead, the relation seems as
inevitable as it is rich in implications:

> They are all gone into the world of light!
> And I alone sit lingring here;
> Their very memory is fair and bright,
> And my sad thoughts doth clear.
>
> It glows and glitters in my cloudy brest
> Like stars upon some gloomy grove,
> Or those faint beams in which this hill is drest,
> After the Sun's remove.[1]

Herbert had little to teach Vaughan about the relation
between God and the created world. He himself contemplated God in the gospel story and in the forms and
ceremonies of the church. He seldom looked at the country-

[1] 'They are all gone into the world of light!'

side; poems in which it figures are rare. There is the savour
of first-hand enjoyment in *Easter*:

> I got me flowers to straw thy way;
> I got me boughs off many a tree:
> But thou wast up by break of day,
> And brought'st thy sweets along with thee.

And in *The Flower* he recognizes the kinship between the
return of spring and the rhythmical recurrences of God's
grace:

> How fresh, O Lord, how sweet and clean
> Are thy returns! ev'n as the flowers in spring;
> To which, besides their own demean,
> The late-past frosts tributes of pleasure bring.
> Grief melts away
> Like snow in May
> As if there were no such cold thing.

In *Easter-wings* the song and flight of the lark have been
perceived as symbols. But these are exceptions in Herbert's
work, whereas for Vaughan, after his 'conversion',

> all the vast expence
> In the Creation shed, and slav'd to sence
> Makes up but lectures for his eie, and ear.[1]

Nature for Vaughan is a revelation of the fulfilment of
God's will. Herbert had envied her constancy; in his poem
Employment (II) he exclaims,

> Oh that I were an Orenge-tree,
> That busie plant!
> Then should I ever laden be,
> And never want
> Some fruit for him that dressed me.

The 'Orenge tree' which bears fruit and blossom at the
same time was an apt illustration for his purpose. Vaughan
looked nearer home and discerned in his immediate sur-
roundings similar grounds for envy.

> I would I were a stone, or tree,
> Or flowre by pedigree,
> Or some poor high-way herb, or Spring
> To flow, or bird to sing!

[1] *The Tempest.*

> Then should I (tyed to one sure state,)
>   All day expect my date;
> But I am sadly loose, and stray
>   A giddy blast each way;
>   O let me not thus range!
>   Thou canst not change.[1]

Again, in *Rules and Lessons*, a poem profoundly influenced by Herbert as regards rhythm and structure, when he speaks of his favourite theme Vaughan is the loving observer of small sights and sounds, he bids man

> Walk with thy fellow-creatures: note the *hush*
> And *whispers* amongst them. There's not a *Spring*
> Or *Leafe* but hath his *Morning-hymn*; each *Bush*
> And *Oak* doth know *I AM*; canst thou not sing?

In *Christs Nativity*, bird song and starlight remind him of the difference between man and the rest of the creation:

> I would I were some *Bird*, or Star,
> Flutt'ring in woods, or lifted far
>   Above this *Inne*
>   And Rode of sin!
> Then either Star, or *Bird*, should be
> Shining, or singing still to thee.

In *Distraction*, starlight, rainbows and the radiance of pearls are envied because, though they spend their light, it does not diminish:
>   Hadst thou
> Made me a starre, a pearle, or a rain-bow,
>   The beames I then had shot
>   My light had lessend not,
>   But now
> I find my selfe the lesse, the more I grow;

Like Wordsworth, Vaughan is tempted to look back to his childhood with regret, because to both poets it seemed that children, like stars or flowers, fulfil the law of their being unconsciously and inevitably. The thought expressed in Vaughan's *Retreat* is, as has often been pointed out, similar in some respects to the thought in Wordsworth's *Intimations of Immortality*; this is due to an essential similarity in

[1] 'And doe they so? have they a Sense.'

79

the outlook of the two poets. Both believe in the creation as the expression of a single mind, they turn to nature, not only to envy and admire, but to discover. Nature is God's book; Wordsworth turns her pages to find the prescriptions of that 'Stern Daughter of the voice of God' whom men call Duty:

> Stern Lawgiver! yet thou dost wear
> The Godhead's most benignant grace;
> Nor know we anything so fair
> As is the smile upon thy face:
> Flowers laugh before thee on their beds
> And fragrance in thy footing treads;
> Thou dost preserve the stars from wrong;
> And the most ancient heavens, through
>   Thee are fresh and strong.[1]

In the same spirit Vaughan contemplates the ordered motions of the stars:

> Fair, order'd lights (whose motion without noise
>   Resembles those true Joys
> Whose spring is on that hil where you do grow
>   And we here tast sometimes below,)
>
> With what exact obedience do you move
>   Now beneath, and now above,
> And in your vast progressions overlook
>   The darkest night, and closest nook!
>
> Some nights I see you in the gladsome East,
>   Some others neer the West,
> And when I cannot see, yet do you shine
>   And beat about your endles line.
>
> Silence, and light, and watchfulnes with you
>   Attend and wind the Clue,
> No sleep, nor sloth assailes you, but poor man
>   Still either sleeps, or slips his span.[2]

Both poets expect to find in nature the secret of that

> something far more deeply interfused
> Whose dwelling is the light of setting suns
> And the round ocean, and the living air,

[1] *Ode to Duty.*   [2] *The Constellation.*

> And the blue sky, and in the mind of man:
> A motion and a spirit, that impels
> All thinking things, all objects of all thought,
> And rolls through all things.[1]

Several of Vaughan's contemporaries observed and enjoyed the world about them (Herrick for instance, and Marvell, and Milton); but Vaughan's nature poetry is different from theirs; he thinks of nature as a source of revelation and could have said with Sir Thomas Browne:

'There are two Books from whence I collect my Divinity; besides that written one of God, another of his servant Nature, that universal and publick Manuscript, that lies expans'd unto the Eyes of all: those that never saw him in the one, have discovered him in the other.'[2]

Even for Traherne, who, among the poets of the century, approaches nearest to Vaughan's attitude, nature is rather a playground than an instructress; she is a delightful gift from God, rather than his interpreter:

> O hevenly Joy!
> O Great and Sacred Blessedness
> Which I possess!
> So great a Joy
> Who did into my Arms convey?
>
> From God abov
> Being sent, the gift doth me enflame
> To prais his Name;
> The Stars do mov,
> The Sun doth shine, to show his Lov.[3]

For Vaughan and later for Wordsworth nature shows not so much the love of God as his mind and meaning. Wordsworth tells us,

> As if awakened, summoned, roused, constrained,
> I looked for universal things; perused
> The common countenance of earth and sky:[4]

[1] *Tintern Abbey.*   [2] *Religio Medici* I xvi.
[3] Thomas Traherne, *Poems of Felicity, The Rapture.*
[4] *The Prelude*, Bk. III, ll. 109, 110.

and Vaughan prays,

> O thou! whose spirit did at first inflame
>   And warm the dead,
> And by a sacred Incubation fed
>   With life this frame
> Which once had neither being, forme, nor name,
>   Grant I may so
>   Thy steps track here below,
>
> That in these Masques and shadows I may see
>   Thy sacred way, . . . [1]

Vaughan observes and often closely imitates the work-manship of Herbert in *Silex Scintillans*, but this attitude to the created world constantly affects his choice and use of imagery. In a poem called *Affliction*, for instance, there is every indication that he has been studying Herbert's poetry, particularly the four poems with this same title, as well as Herbert's *Deniall*. The theme is similar to that of Herbert's *Affliction* (I). Both poets are contemplating the suffering with which God purges his elect. The opening lines are in that staccato speech accent, which Herbert adapted from Donne:

> Peace, peace; It is not so. Thou doest miscall
>   Thy Physick; Pils that change
> Thy sick Accessions into setled health,
> This is the great *Elixir* that turns gall
> To wine and sweetness; Poverty to wealth,
>   And brings man home, when he doth range.

The device, used by Herbert in *Deniall* and elsewhere, of making an imperfect rhyme scheme reflect an inharmonious mood, is here adapted by Vaughan. He stresses the irregu-larities of his metrical pattern until the end, when it is regularized to represent the return of peace. But the differ-ence between Vaughan's poem and any of Herbert's is far more essential than the resemblance. Whereas Herbert may chance to draw a simile from nature, attaching no more

---

[1] 'I walkt the other day (to spend my hour,).'

importance to it than that it affords the resemblance he requires:

> We are the trees whom shaking fastens more;

or
>   Dissolve the knot
> As the sunne scatters by his light
> All the rebellions of the night;

Vaughan sees in such parallels a revelation of unity between the pattern of the world and the ordering of men's souls:

> Did not he, who ordain'd the day,
>   Ordain night too?
> And in the greater world display
> What in the lesser he would do?
> All flesh is Clay, thou know'st; and but that God
>   Doth use his rod,
> And by a fruitfull Change of frosts, and showres
>   Cherish, and bind thy *powr's*,
> Thou wouldst to weeds, and thistles quite disperse,
>   And be more wild than is thy verse.
>
>   .   .   .   .   .   .
>
> Were all the year one constant Sun-shine, wee
>   Should have no flowres,
> All would be drought, and leanness; not a tree
>   Would make us bowres;
>
>   .   .   .   .   .   .
>
> Thus doth God *Key* disorder'd man
>   (Which none else can,)
> Tuning his brest to rise, or fall;
> And by a sacred, needfull art
> Like strings, stretch ev'ry part
> Making the whole most Musicall.[1]

Vaughan lays stress upon the repetition in the microcosm of the pattern of the macrocosm.

The Morning-watch, perhaps the most perfect whole among all Vaughan's poems (for he is often fragmentary), seems to have developed out of a chance phrase of Herbert's. Herbert's poem, *Prayer* (I), is a rapid succession of similes; among other things prayer is likened to

> A kinde of tune which all things heare and fear.

---

[1] *Affliction.*

Here is the poem which this line apparently suggested to Vaughan.

The Morning-watch

O Joyes! Infinite sweetnes! with what flowres,
And shoots of glory, my soul breakes, and buds!
   All the long houres
   Of night, and Rest
   Through the still shrouds
   Of sleep, and Clouds,
  This Dew fell on my Breast;
   O how it *Blouds*
And *Spirits* all my Earth! heark! In what Rings,
And *Hymning Circulations* the quick world
   Awakes, and sings;
   The rising winds,
   And falling springs,
   Birds, beasts, all things
  Adore him in their kinds.
   Thus all is hurl'd
In sacred *Hymnes*, and *Order*, The great *Chime*
And *Symphony* of nature. Prayer is
   The world in tune,
   A spirit-voyce,
   And vocall joyes
  Whose Echo is heav'ns blisse.
   O let me climbe
When I lye down! The Pious soul by night
Is like a clouded starre, whose beames though sed
   To shed their light
   Under some Cloud
   Yet are above
   And shine, and move
  Beyond that mistie shrowd.
   So in my Bed
That Curtain'd grave, though sleep, like ashes, hide
My lamp, and life, both shall in thee abide.[1]

---

[1] In the lines 'O how it Blouds...Hymning Circulations...' Vaughan combines the old and new physiology. According to the old belief, from the blood 'spirits are first begotten in the heart, which afterwards by the arteries are communicated to the other parts' (Burton's *Anatomy of Melancholy*, Part I, Sect. 1, Member II). Compare Donne's *The Extasie*, lines 61–64, 'As our blood labours to beget / Spirits as like soules as it can / Because such fingers need to knit / That subtile Knot, which makes us

This is a very different way of recasting another poet's phrase, from that exemplified in the *Lines to Amoret*. The lines borrowed from Donne lost their original vigour and gained nothing new from Vaughan's poem. But Herbert's chance phrase is transformed into the focal point of an apprehension of the world, which Herbert had not developed and perhaps not thought of. His influence on Vaughan cannot be overstated in so far as it directed him to the contemplation from which his poetry was to spring; but it can be misstated if the wrong kind of importance is attached to the verbal resemblances. Herbert may have made Vaughan a poet, but he did not make him in his own image. Vaughan is weak where Herbert is strong, and strong where he is weak. He lacks form, order, economy, he seldom knows where to stop; whereas the perfection of form is characteristic of Herbert's poetry. On the other hand Vaughan has a gift of song which Herbert often lacks. He can convey the ecstasy of joy or grief or worship by the movement of the verse, and he has a stronger instinct than Herbert for the magic of words and phrases. A selection of the best from Herbert would be a selection of poems, a selection of the best from Vaughan would include some single stanzas, lines, or even half lines.

Among these would be several that were suggested to him by Herbert. 'Prayer is the world in tune' would need to be set in its context to convey all the meaning Vaughan perceived in it. Other phrases can be enjoyed in isolation. A phrase which to Herbert was only an essential part of the structure of a poem, was sometimes picked out by Vaughan

man....' William Harvey's discovery of the circulation of the blood was published in 1628. Vaughan, himself a physician, would presumably have been interested. In these lines both the blood-begotten vital spirits and the circular movement of the blood represent the revitalizing of the poet and of the rest of the created world, at dawn. Vaughan often italicizes words to which he wants to draw the reader's attention, but no critic, as far as I know, has especially attended to the relation between *Blouds-Spirits-Hymning Circulations*.

and lovingly worked on till it satisfied his ear. Herbert had written, in a poem called *The Familie*,

> Joyes oft are there, and griefs as oft as joyes;
> But griefs without a noise;
> Yet speak they louder then distemper'd fears.
> What is so shrill as silent tears?

Vaughan, in *Olor Iscanus* (1651), in *An Epitaph upon the Lady Elizabeth*, made his first attempt to incorporate Herbert's phrase:

> Thy portion here was *griefe*, thy years
> Distilld no other rain, but tears,
> Tears without noise, but (understood)
> As lowd, and shrill as any bloud;

It was not very successful and the words still haunted him. In *Silex Scintillans*, in a poem called *Admission*, he found their final form:

> How shril are silent teares? . . .

It is the first half of a line of a poem which does not fulfil its promise; but the history of the line shows an interest in the choice and arrangement of words to produce an emotional impact. The magic of the phrase is Vaughan's, though it owes something to Herbert which is of vital importance. Vaughan learnt from Herbert the value of under-emphasis. He learnt to lead his reader on with commonplace words in a prose order until, all unprepared, he is brought up short by some startlingly poignant phrase. Instead of being first lifted out of the rut of triviality by the poet's emphasis and solemnity, he is shown the problems of life, death, time and eternity within the orbit of his daily experience. To speak familiarly of ultimate things is the prerogative of the metaphysical poets. Their habit of connecting the temporal and the eternal made it possible for them. It is not with any intention of avoiding the trivial that Vaughan most frequently expresses himself in terms of light and stars and running water; these were the stuff of his daily experience. He assimilated and adapted the manner of Herbert, which Herbert in turn had learnt from Donne. Without ceremony, as it were casually, these poets plunge us into the problems that baffle thought; so Donne,

> What if this present were the worlds last night?

or Herbert,

> Lord, how can man preach thy eternal word?

and Vaughan, in the same tradition, gives us,

> I saw Eternity the other night
> Like a great *Ring* of pure and endless light,
>   All calm, as it was bright,
> And round beneath it, Time in hours, days, years
>   Driv'n by the spheres
> Like a vast shadow mov'd, In which the world
>   And all her train were hurl'd;...[1]

Here is no imitation, but Vaughan has been able to assimilate the influence of Donne, just as Herbert, with his different outlook and temperament, had assimilated it. The problem of time haunted Vaughan. Few poets have phrased more beautifully the experience of time-bound man striving to apprehend eternity; or of the bewildering variation in the rate at which time passes:

> Silence, and stealth of dayes! 'Tis now
>   Since thou art gone,
> Twelve hundred houres...

is the opening of a poem about the death of his brother. For Donne, the 'houres, dayes, moneths...are the rags of time', for Vaughan,

>   Heav'n
> Is a plain watch and without figures winds
> All ages up; who drew this Circle even
> He fills it; Dayes, and hours are *Blinds*.[2]

Donne's influence over this school of poetry was very great; but each of his followers who deserves separate

---

[1] *The World.*   [2] *The Evening-watch. A Dialogue.*

attention contributed something of his own to the tradition. Vaughan brought a new range of experience within the compass of this style. No one else among Donne's followers watched the earth, sky, and water, the birds and flowers with the same emotion, nor with the same delicacy of observation. Vaughan lacked Donne's vigorous and varied awareness of human character and affairs; he lacked Herbert's sobriety and exquisite sense of form, his undeviating control of powerful feeling; but often his poetry has a radiance and a movement which neither of these attempts. Vaughan, who resembles Wordsworth in his nature mysticism, sometimes resembles Shelley in the ecstatic outpouring of his numbers. He is more lyrical than his masters. Perhaps he is less restrained by intellectual perplexity. He could immerse himself in rapturous contemplation of dawn or sunset. Neither Donne nor Herbert could have written *The Dawning*: but Vaughan would not have written it as he did had he not learnt from them and assimilated the metaphysical influence. It is a song of rapture, but with an intellectual ground base.

> Ah! what time wilt thou come? when shall that crie
>   The *Bridegroom's Comming!* fil the sky?
>   Shall it in the Evening run
>   When our words and works are done?
>   Or wil thy all-surprizing light
>   Break at midnight?
>   When either sleep, or some dark pleasure
>   Possesseth mad man without measure;
>   Or shal these early, fragrant hours
>   Unlock thy bowres?
>   And with their blush of light descry
>   Thy locks crown'd with eternitie;
>   Indeed, it is the only time
>   That with thy glory doth best chime,
>   All now are stirring, ev'ry field
>   Ful hymns doth yield,
>   The whole Creation shakes off night,
>   And for thy shadow looks the light,

Stars now vanish without number,
Sleepie Planets set, and slumber,
The pursie Clouds disband, and scatter,
All expect some sudden matter,
Not one beam triumphs, but from far
        That morning-star.

From first to last Vaughan laid himself open to the influence of other poets, but he emerged with a way of perceiving and of expressing his perceptions which bore his own hallmark.

CHAPTER VI

RICHARD CRASHAW, 1613?–1649

That our sensuality by the vertue of Christ's Passion, be
brought up into the substance.

CRESSY, *Revelation of Divine Love*

IN so far as we read poetry to discover what the poet
meant, as much as, or at least as well as, what his poem
may mean to us, his biography is a useful crutch. We
know little of Crashaw's life beyond the bare outline; but
that little helps us to envisage the man who wrote the
poems. His mother died when he was a baby, the exact date
is unknown, but he had a step-mother by the time he was
seven years old, and she died a year later. During that brief
space we are told that she showed a 'singular motherly
affection for the child of her predecessor'. Other women
befriended him when he grew up. He speaks with warm
and reverent affection of the Mother of a Community, who
was possibly Mary Collet, the niece of Nicholas Ferrar of
Little Gidding; she is described by him, in a letter, as 'the
gentlest, kindest, most tender-hearted and liberall handed
soul I think this day alive'. The Countess of Denbigh and
Queen Henrietta Maria were good to him and recommended
him for preferment at Rome; but he was never to find

> That not impossible shee
> That shall command my heart and mee;[1]

and the fact that he was appointed to a College Fellowship
in 1635 (when he was twenty-two years old), and that he
continued to prefer the monastic life, 'a little contentfull
kingdom' as he describes it, suggests that he never
seriously sought her. For Crashaw, as for Herbert, religion
supplied the only outlet for an emotional nature. Yet the

[1] *Wishes, To his (supposed) Mistresse.*

two poets were so different in temperament that, although both wrote love poems to God and both were influenced in some degree by the prevailing poetic fashion, their poetry has little in common.

Crashaw's father, William Crashaw, was a puritan parson, and wrote anti-papal pamphlets of some violence. It has been suggested that Crashaw's own Roman leanings were due to a reaction from parental authority; but as his father, who died when Richard was only thirteen, was a man of sufficiently catholic sympathies to translate Jesuit hymns to the Virgin from 'the most mistie times of Popery', it seems on the whole more likely that Crashaw inherited from his father the temperament that led him first to Laudian high churchmanship, and finally to Roman Catholicism.

The boy was sent to the Charterhouse School after his father's death and from thence to Pembroke College, Cambridge, as an Exhibitioner, in 1631. Almost at once he began to write elegies in English and Latin. It is improbable that he felt much for the deaths of Dr Samuel Brooke or Dr Mansell; they merely provided him with an opportunity to exercise his talent. The death of Michael Chambers, a young Fellow of Queens', and of 'the most desired Mr Herrys', Fellow of Pembroke, are in a different case. These two were akin to him in their youthfulness and in their service of the muses. They were in much the same relation to him as Henry King was to Milton, and Crashaw, like Milton, dwells on the frustrated hopes of those who had expected their talents to bear fruit:

> For Life by volumes lengthened
> A Line or two, to speake him dead.
> For the Laurell in his verse,
> The sullen Cypresse o're his Herse.
> For a silver-crowned Head
> A durty pillow in Death's Bed.
> For so deare, so deep a trust,
> Sad requitall, thus much dust![1]

[1] *Upon the Death of a Gentleman.*

He wrote five poems inspired by the death of Herrys and there are lines in each of them that foreshadow his maturer poetry. They display his propensity for nursing an emotion and savouring all the sweetness of grief, and they show also Crashaw's habit of worrying out of his conceits their emotional and sensational, rather than their intellectual, implications:

> The fresh hopes of his lovely Youth,
> Flourisht in so faire a grouth.
> So sweet the Temple was, that shrin'd
> The Sacred sweetnesse of his mind.
> That could the Fates know to relent?
> Could they know what mercy meant;
> Or had ever learnt to beare,
> The soft tincture of a Teare:
> Teares would now have flow'd so deepe,
> As might have taught Griefe how to weepe.
> Now all their steely operation,
> Would quite have lost the cruell fashion.
> Sicknesse would have gladly been,
> Sick himself to have sav'd him:
> And his Feaver wish'd to prove
> Burning, onely in his Love.[1]

The last image inevitably suggests a comparison with Donne's impassioned intellectual paradoxes in *A Feaver*, and especially with the stanza in which he recognizes the fever as a like-minded rival:

> Yet 'twas of my minde, seizing thee,
>   Though it in thee cannot persever.
> For I had rather owner bee
>   Of thee one houre, than all else ever.

But the difference between the two poets in their handling of the conceit is far more striking than their resemblance in its conception. Crashaw slowly elaborates an hypothesis, he has time to dwell on the sweetness of the mind and of the body that enshrined it, to picture the 'soft' tears of the

---

[1] *Another* (on the death of Mr Herrys).

Fates, the weeping of Sorrow, the sickness of Sickness and
the burning love of Feaver, while Donne rushes from one
intellectual hyperbole to another including, as is his habit,
a wide range of speculation within the single experience:

> O wrangling schooles, that search what fire
>   Shall burne this world, had none the wit
> Unto this knowledge to aspire,
>   That this her feaver might be it?
>
> And yet shee cannot wast by this,
>   Nor long beare this torturing wrong,
> For much corruption needfull is
>   To fuell such a feaver long.

The conceit of the Feaver as a lover is only one of a
series of situations that Donne invents, in order to develop
his hypothesis that his mistress cannot die. The Feaver can
only enjoy his love for a moment because

> much corruption needfull is
>   To fuell such a feaver long,

therefore

> These burning fits but meteors bee,
> Whose matter in thee is soone spent,

and from this again it follows logically that the 'feaver'
must be of the same mind as the poet and prefer to enjoy
her, though it be only for a moment. In Crashaw's poem
there is no logical chain of connection, but only a succession
of emotional scenes.

These elegies were not the only poems Crashaw wrote
at Pembroke; his lines *Upon the gunpowder treason*, while
they demonstrate that he was not as yet conscious of
Roman Catholic sympathies, display also another aspect of
the sensationalism which was to remain an outstanding
characteristic of his poetry:

> Grow plumpe, leane Death; his Holinesse a feast
> Hath now praepar'd, & you must be his guest.

Come grimme destruction, & in purple gore
Dye seu'n times deeper then they were before
Thy scarlet robes. for heere you must not share
A common banquett. noe, heere's princely fare.

. . . . . .

But dares destruction eate these candid breasts,
The Muses, & the Graces sugred neasts?[1]
Dares hungry death snatch of one cherry lipp?
Or thirsty treason offer once to sippe
One dropp of this pure Nectar, which doth flow
In azure channells warme through mounts of snow?

. . . . . .

Poore meagre horror streightwaies was amaz'd
And in the stead of feeding stood, & gaz'd.
Their appetites were gone at th' uery sight;
But yet their eyes surfett with sweet delight.
Only the Pope a stomack still could find;
But yett they were not powder'd to his mind.

It may seem unfair to dwell upon so early and so crude
a poem, and one which Crashaw would have repudiated
later for its sentiments. But its faults are of a kind that he
never outgrew and that differentiate him sharply from
Donne and from Donne's imitators. Whereas they tend to
over-elaborate an idea, Crashaw loves to elaborate sensations. Moreover, his sensations are peculiar and sometimes
repellent. The collocation of torture and erotic emotion in
this poem is of a kind that occurs repeatedly in Crashaw's
poetry from first to last. There can be no doubt that the
conjunction of physical torture with sensual love was to
him pleasurable and inevitable; compare for instance the
third and fourth stanzas of *On the wounds of our crucified
Lord*.

O thou that on this foot hast laid
    Many a kisse, and many a Teare,
Now thou shal't have all repaid,
    Whatsoe're thy charges were.

[1] The nature of the pun here, while it is in the fashion of the time, is
peculiarly to Crashaw's own taste.

94

> This foot hath got a Mouth and lippes,
>   To pay the sweet summe of thy kisses:
> To pay thy Teares, an Eye that weeps
>   In stead of Teares such Gems as this is.

In such ways as these Crashaw's early College poems fore-tell the future characteristics of his verse and mark the lines along which he was to diverge from the Donne tradition.

There is no evidence of Roman Catholic leanings during his years at Cambridge but he was throughout under the influence of the high Church and Royalist party and he was, as we should expect, particularly interested in a decorative, ritualistic form of worship. He wrote complimentary verses to Laney, the Master of Pembroke, praising him for restoring the beauty of the College chapel and its worship, and also to his tutor Tournay, who was refused the degree of B.D. for impugning the puritan doctrine of justification by faith, and in about the year 1635 Crashaw moved over from Pembroke to Peterhouse, which was then the centre of Laudian high-churchmanship. Here he seems to have been actively concerned in decorating the new chapel and also to have been noted for his ascetic devotions in the church of Little St Mary's, which served as Peterhouse Chapel until the new one was ready:

> There he made his nest more gladly then David's Swallow neere the house of God: where like a primitive Saint, he offered more prayers in the night, then others usually offer in the day.[1]

He remained at Peterhouse until 1643 and there two poets were his friends, Joseph Beaumont, Fellow of Peterhouse from 1636–44, and Cowley, who came up in 1637. Neither of these seems to have influenced his poetry very much, it was of far greater importance that during these years he acquired the Spanish and Italian languages. This meant that he could read the Spanish mystics and the biographies

[1] *Steps to the Temple.* The Preface to the Reader, 1648.

of the recently canonized Saint Teresa (canonized in 1622) and that he could steep himself in the 'hyperboles and luscious sweetness of the Italian poet Marino'. These are the influences that are most manifest upon the thought and style of his poetry and that in part account for its deviation from any of the dominant schools of poetry in the England of his day.

Crashaw enjoyed eight years of peaceful study and contemplation at Peterhouse, but by 1643 Cambridge had become uninhabitable for a high-churchman and a Royalist. Cosin, the Master of Peterhouse, was expelled for sending the College plate to the king at York in 1643, and in the same year Crashaw was at Leyden from whence he wrote a long letter to a friend at Cambridge. The main purpose of the letter was to make arrangements whereby he might one day hope to return to Peterhouse for, he writes,

> I haue I assure you no desire to be absolutely and irrespectiuely rid of my beloued Patrimony in St Peter. No man then myself holds more high the humble sceptre of such a little contenfull kingdom. And as safely may I say no man more unprouided of any present course.

But there was to be no return. Crashaw's movements in the next few years cannot be certainly known. It is probable that he went for a time to Oxford, where the court had been established. If so he would there have become acquainted with the Countess of Denbigh to whom he dedicated the revised edition of his sacred poems, *Carmen Deo Nostro*:

> To my Lady the Covntesse of Denbigh by her most devoted servant. R.C. In hearty acknowledgment of his immortall obligation to her Goodnes & Charity.

Here also he would have met his other protectress, Queen Henrietta Maria.

But all this is conjectural. The next time Crashaw is referred to in contemporary documents after the letter from Leyden, is in a letter from his friend Cowley. Cowley crossed over to France in 1646 as secretary to Lord Jermyn, the minister in attendance on Queen Henrietta Maria. He found Crashaw in Paris 'being a meere scholar and very shiftless' and it may have been he who recommended him to the notice of the queen. Crashaw's conversion to Roman Catholicism must have taken place during the obscure years in his biography between 1643 and 1646, since his *Steps to the Temple* published in 1646 contains the apology for the Hymn to St Teresa 'being written while he was yet among the protestants'. In 1646 the queen wrote a letter recommending Crashaw to the care of the Pope and with it he set out for Rome. There was some delay during which Crashaw's poverty was unrelieved and then, in 1647, he was found by Dr John Bargrave in the service of Cardinal Palotto. Bargrave gives an account of the last three years of Crashaw's life:

When I went first of my four times to Rome there were four revolters to the Roman Church that had been fellows of Peterhouse in Cambridge with myself. The name of one of them was Mr R. Crashaw who was...one of the followers of this Cardinal.... Mr Crashaw infinitely commended his Cardinal but complained extremely of the wickedness of those of his retinue of which he, having the Cardinal's ear, complained to him. Upon which the Italians fell so far out with him that the Cardinal, to secure his life, was fain to put him from his service, and procuring him some small imploy at the Lady's of Loretto; whither he went in pilgrimmage in summer time, and, overheating himself died in four weeks after he came thither, and it was doubtful whether he were not poisoned.

From these sparse events and from the few contemporary references to Crashaw, we see him as a man of rare singlemindedness. He continually directed himself towards a mode of life which would afford him peace and leisure for contemplation. The world did not tempt him. Severed from the shelter of his College Chapel and of friends like-minded with himself, he sought the protection and support of the Roman Catholic Church. He seems always to have starved himself of bodily comfort and to have cared only for comfort of the spirit. His friends thought him indifferent to all that the world has to offer. Thomas Car, in verses introducing the first edition of *Carmen Deo Nostro*, 1652, describes him for us:

> To witt, being pleas'd with all things, he pleas'd all;
> Nor would he giue, nor take offence; befall
> What might; he would possesse himselfe: and liue
> As deade (deuoyde of interest) t'all might giue
> Desease t'his well-composed mynd, forestal'd
> With heauenly riches, which had wholy call'd
> His thoughtes from earth, to liue aboue in'th air,
> A very bird of paradice. No care
> Had he of earthly trashe. What might suffice
> To fitt his soule to heauenly exercise
> Sufficed him; and may we guesse his hart
> By what his lipps brings forth, his onely part
> Is God and godly thoughtes. Leaues doubt to none
> But that to him one God is all; all's one.
> What he might eate or weare he tooke no thought;
> His needfull foode he rather found then sought.
> He seekes no downes, no sheetes, his bed's still made;
> If he can find a chaire or stoole, he's layd;
> When day peepes in, he quitts his restlesse rest,
> And still, poore soul, before he's vp he's dres't.

    .   .   .   .   .

From the time he left Cambridge he was miserably poor, except for the few years under Palotto's protection, and this he sacrificed because he would not tolerate the 'wickedness' of his fellow-attendants. The sole satisfaction he allowed to his sensual and emotional needs was poetry, and in his poetry the senses and the emotions had their revenge.

When Crashaw turns to poetry his attention fixes itself on the particular sensation he contemplates. The poem *On the wounds of our crucified Lord*, already quoted, may seem an extreme example; but the treatment of the theme is typical of Crashaw's method. He dwells on the actual wounds and their texture and seeks to communicate the horror and pity of the particular moment. Herbert handles the same theme in *Good Friday*; but in him it arouses a series of thoughts instead of a series of sensual and emotional impressions:

> Shall I thy woes
> Number according to thy foes?
> Or, since one starre show'd thy first breath,
>   Shall all thy death?
>
> Or shall each leaf
> Which falls in Autumne, score a grief?
> Or can not leaves, but fruit, be signe
>   Of the true vine?

This is poetry learnt in the school of Donne, in which a conceit is the starting point of cogitation. The same kind of comparison can be drawn between Crashaw's *The Weeper* and either Donne's *A Valediction: of weeping* or Marvell's *Eyes and Tears*. For Donne and for Marvell the visual image of the tear suggests a series of thoughts logically connected with the shape, texture or behaviour of tears. But in Crashaw's poem one sensual image gives rise only to another. The senses remain dominant; if we move away from the tears of the Magdalene it is not to some thought they suggest, some generalization about the nature of love or sorrow, but to another image which has for Crashaw the same tender sweetness:

> The dew no more will weepe,
> The Primroses pale cheeke to decke,
> The deaw no more will sleepe,
> Nuzzel'd in the Lillies necke.
> Much rather would it tremble heere,
> And leave them both to bee thy Teare.
>
> Not the soft Gold which
> Steales from the Amber-weeping Tree,
> Makes sorrow halfe so Rich,
> As the drops distil'd from thee.
> Sorrowes best Iewels lye in these
> Caskets, of which Heaven keeps the Keyes.

When sorrow would be seene
In her brightest Majesty,
(For shee is a Queen)
Then is shee drest by none but thee.
Then, and onely then shee weares
Her richest Pearles, I meane thy Teares.

Not in the Evenings Eyes
When they red with weeping are,
For the Sun that dyes,
Sits sorrow with a face so faire.
Nowhere but heere did ever meet
Sweetnesse so sad, sadnes so sweet.

The nestling image in the first stanza,

The deaw no more will sleepe
Nuzzel'd in the Lillies necke,

brings to the mind a procession of similar images in
Crashaw's poetry, images of nests and other soft secret
refuges, in which shelter, warmth and sweetness are found.
In the poem *To the Name above every Name, the Name
of Jesus*, the word 'nest' occurs five times, with this meaning
more or less explicit; the following are two typical examples:

All ye wise SOVLES, who in the wealthy Brest
Of this vnbounded NAME build your warm Nest.

ll. 11, 12.

Our Murmurs haue their Musick too,
Ye mighty ORBES, as well as you;
Nor yeilds the noblest Nest
Of warbling SERAPHIM to the eares of Loue,
A choicer Lesson then the ioyfull BREST
Of a poor panting Turtle-Doue.

ll. 103 ff.

It will be noticed here and elsewhere in Crashaw's poetry
that the words nest and breast or bosom are closely associated, they are alternate symbols of protection and fostering
love. In *Sancta Maria Dolorum* he writes,

O Mother turtle-doue!
Soft sourse of love

> That these dry lidds might borrow
> Somthing from thy full Seas of sorrow!
> O in that brest
> Of thine (the noblest nest
> Both of loue's fires & flouds) might I recline
> This hard, cold, Heart of mine!

In the nativity hymn the chorus of Angels sings,

> We saw thee in thy baulmy Nest,
> Young dawn of our aeternal Day![1]

But the meaning that nestling imagery has for Crashaw is perhaps most fully brought out in the second stanza of *Vexilla Regis. The Hymn of the Holy Crosse:*

> Lo, how the streames of life, from that full nest
> Of loues, thy lord's too liberall brest,
> Flow in an amorous floud
> Of WATER wedding BLOOD.
> With these he wash't thy stain, transfer'd thy smart,
> And took it home to his own heart.

To return to the stanzas of *The Weeper* which gave rise to this digression. Crashaw succeeds, in the stanzas quoted, in expressing the particular quality of emotion he experiences in contemplating the Magdalene. In them he develops a picture of delicate, grave, queenly sorrow, enviable in its utter abandon. Other stanzas which precede and follow it in the poem are less successful and have been deservedly ridiculed, for example, stanzas 4 and 5:

> Vpwards thou dost weep.
> Heaun's bosome drinks the gentle stream.
> Where th'milky riuers creep,
> Thine floates aboue; & is the cream.
> Waters aboue th'Heauns, what they be
> We'are taught best by thy TEARES & thee.
>
> Euery morn from hence
> A brisk Cherub somthing sippes

---

[1] *In The Holy Nativity of our Lord God. A Hymn sung as by the Shepherds*, ll. 31–2.

> Whose sacred influence
> Addes sweetnes to his sweetest Lippes.
> Then to his musick. And his song
> Tasts of this Breakfast all day long.

It is not merely our own commonplace associations with, for instance, the word breakfast, that makes the stanzas unacceptable; it is Crashaw's mercilessly minute dwelling on sensations, unrelated to thought. The same fault is to be found with his unnecessarily concrete development of an image (which he added to the poem when he revised it) of the Magdalene's eyes as

> Two walking baths; two weeping motions;
> Portable, & compendious oceans.

It is doubtful whether a poet in whom the senses and the emotions were so much more active than the intellect, was well served by the metaphysical style.

The metaphysical conceit at its most effective is a focal point at which emotion, sense-impression and thought are perceived as one. Sense-impression is controlled and limited by the context; for instance, in the second stanza of Donne's *Funerall*,

> For if the sinewy thread my braine lets fall
>   Through every part,
> Can tye those parts, and make mee one of all;
> These haires which upward grew, and strength and art
>   Have from a better braine,
> Can better do'it . . .

The connection between the 'sinewy thread' or spinal cord, centre of the nervous system, and 'those haires which upward grew' is perceived by the intellect; it is, and this is not uncommon with Donne, rather impeded than otherwise by strong visual imagery; what the reader perceives is more a diagram than a picture. Sometimes, on the other hand, a metaphysical conceit demands a response from the senses and the intellect, but makes no impact on the emotions; for instance, Donne's conceit in *Communitie*,

> But they are ours as fruits are ours,
> He that but tasts, he that devours,
> And he that leaves all, doth as well:
> Chang'd loves are but chang'd sorts of meat,
> And when hee hath the kernell eate,
> Who doth not fling away the shell?

But the element that is always present and that distinguishes Donne's conceits and those of his followers from other types of conceit, is the intellectual element. For Donne such an instrument was peculiarly apt and necessary. His mind was constantly spurred to fresh activity by sensation or by emotion, and the total experience resulting could only be conveyed in the metaphysical conceit. Herbert made more sparing use of it; but at times a conceit of this nature enabled him to pass from description or analysis to synthesis. For instance, in the poem *Content,* where he describes and meditates about the contented soul, his contemplation culminates in a series of conceits in which the thought is identified with sensations and their corresponding emotions:

> This soul doth span the world, and hang content
> From either pole unto the centre;
> Where in each room of the well-furnisht tent
> He lies warm and without adventure.
>
> The brags of life are but a nine dayes wonder;
> And after death the fumes that spring
> From private bodies make as big a thunder
> As those which rise from a huge King.
>
> Onely thy Chronicle is lost; and yet
> Better by worms be all once spent
> Then to have hellish moths still gnaw and fret
> Thy name in books, which may not rent:
>
> When all thy deeds, whose brunt thou feel'st alone,
> Are chaw'd by others pens and tongue;
> And as their wit is, their digestion,
> Thy nourisht fame is weak or strong.

The attitude here adopted was the consequence of thought and the logic of the images continues the activity which gave rise to them. Crashaw's images, on the other hand, arise directly out of his emotional needs. A passage from *To the Name above every Name, the Name of Jesus*, will illustrate the difference:

> Little, alas, thought They
> Who tore the Fair Brests of thy Freinds,
>   Their Fury but made way
> For Thee; And seru'd therein Thy glorious ends.
> What did Their weapons but with wider pores
> Inlarge thy flaming-brested Louers
>   More freely to transpire
>   That impatient Fire
> The Heart that hides Thee hardly couers.
> What did their Weapons but sett wide the Doores
> For Thee: Fair, purple Doores, of loue's deuising;
> The Ruby windowes which inrich't the EAST
> Of Thy so oft repeated Rising.
> Each wound of Theirs was Thy new Morning;
> And reinthron'd thee in thy Rosy Nest,
> With blush of thine own Blood thy day adorning,
> It was the witt of loue o'reflowd the Bounds
> Of WRATH, & made thee way through All Those
>   WOUNDS.

These conceits are undoubtedly focal points of Crashaw's experience; but what elements are united in them? Their elements are sensations and emotions. Yet, in a sense, they are metaphysical, for it is the intellect that operates the union. It is by a logical device that he unites in them the sensation of love and the sensation of pain. This is the peculiarity of his conceits, sharply differentiating them from those of Donne, Herbert or Vaughan. The intellect is operative, not before or after, but only in the moment of apprehending the image. By its means he contrives images which satisfy his emotional needs. The images of the ascetic Crashaw are far more predominantly sexual than those of Donne, who had known the pleasures of sensuality, or of Herbert, who never seems to have desired them. He constantly identifies the processes of conception, birth and fostering, with the love that unites God and the saints. The function of the intellect in his poetry is to give logical coherence to his perception of identity between these things. What is meant can be made plain by a series of examples. The first is from the poem just quoted. He is addressing the dawn of that day which is to bring the name of Christ to earth:

> Lo where it comes, vpon The snowy DOVE's
> Soft Back; And brings a Bosom big with Loues.
> WELCOME to our dark world, Thou
>   Womb of Day!
> Vnfold thy fair Conceptions; And display
> The Birth of our Bright Ioyes.

A similar conceit is developed in the first stanza of *Easter Day*:

> Rise, Heire of fresh Eternity,
>   From thy Virgin Tombe:
> Rise mighty man of wonders, and thy world with thee
>   Thy Tombe, the universall East,
>   Natures new wombe,
> Thy Tombe, faire Immortalities perfumed Nest.

In the last stanza of *The Hymn of Sainte Thomas in Adoration of the Blessed Sacrament* he develops the parallel between God's love for man and maternal love, the source of nourishment. The image here is not of suckling at the breast but of the sacrificial nourishing attributed to the pelican, by means of which Crashaw is again able to identify love and physical pain:

> O soft self-wounding Pelican!
> Whose brest weepes Balm for wounded man.
> Ah this way bend thy benign floud
> To'a bleeding Heart that gaspes for blood.
> That blood, whose least drops soueraign be
> To wash my worlds of sins from me.
> Come love! Come LORD! & that long day
> For which I languish, come away.
> When this dry soul those eyes shall see,

And drink the vnseal'd sourse of thee.
When Glory's sun faith's shades shall chase,
And for thy veil giue me thy FACE.

The conceits in all three instances are metaphysical in so far as they depend upon logical connections; reasoned analysis brings out their full meaning. But the function of the intellect in Crashaw's poetry is to justify an unusual collocation of sensations.

A Hymn to The Name and Honor of the Admirable Sainte Teresa is the poem of Crashaw's which has rightly attracted most readers. It is his most complete and adequate expression of his own religious experience. In it he makes little use of intellectual conceits because he had little need for them. The theme itself involved the conjunction of feelings that most moved him. He had only to tell his story and, in the telling, to convey what it meant to him:

Love, thou art Absolute sole lord
Of LIFE & DEATH. To proue the word,
Wee'l now appeal to none of all
Those thy old Souldiers, Great & tall,
Ripe Men of Martyrdom, that could reach down
With strong armes, their triumphant crown;
Such as could with lusty breath
Speak lowd into the face of death
Their Great LORD's glorious name, to none
Of those whose spatious Bosomes spread a throne
For LOVE at larg to fill: spare blood & sweat;
And see him take a priuate seat,
Making his mansion in the mild
And milky soul of a soft child.
    Scarse had she learn't to lisp the name
Of Martyr; yet she thinks it shame
Life should so long play with that breath
Which spent can buy so braue a death.
She neuer vndertook to know
What death with loue should haue to doe;
Nor has she e're yet vnderstood
Why to show loue, she should shed blood
Yet though she cannot tell you why,
She can LOVE, & she can DY.

It is in this poem that Crashaw best succeeds in communicating to his reader his own attitude towards martyrdom, an attitude not merely of admiration but of envy. It is the luxury of pain that we feel in the lines:

> O how oft shalt thou complain
> Of a sweet & subtle PAIN.
> Of intolerable IOYES;
> Of a DEATH, in which who dyes
> Loues his death, and dyes again.
> And would for euer so be slain.
> And liues, & dyes; and knowes not why
> To liue, But that he thus may neuer leaue to DY.

The consummation of her martyrdom he can best express in terms of consummated love:

> O what delight, when reveal'd LIFE shall stand
> And teach thy lipps heav'n with his hand;
> On which thou now maist to thy wishes
> Heap up thy consecrated kisses.
>
> .   .   .   .   .   .
>
> Thou shalt look round about, and see
> Thousands of crown'd Soules throng to be
> Themselves thy crown.. Sons of thy vowes
> The virgin-births with which thy sovereign spouse
> Made fruitful thy fair soul,

Crashaw wrote two more poems inspired by Saint Teresa, *An Apologie for the Fore-going Hymne as having been writt when the author was yet among the protestantes* and *The Flaming Heart upon the Book and Picture of the Seraphicall Saint Teresa*. Neither of these is as sustained a lyrical outburst as the first; but in the closing lines of the last poem the harmony of theme, mood and manner are once more perfectly achieved. They are the loveliest lines Crashaw ever wrote and perhaps the lines in which he most easily and fully expressed himself. They raise once more the question whether the peculiar qualities of Donne's style: intellectual imagery, logical forms and speech rhythms, were of any service to Crashaw. Was he not at his best when he least needed or employed them; when, as here, he could dispense with the intricacies of the conceit and 'pour out his full heart'?

O thou vndanted daughter of desires!
By all thy dowr of LIGHTS & FIRES;
By all the eagle in thee, all the doue;
By all thy liues & deaths of loue;
By thy larg draughts of intellectuall day,
And by thy thirsts of loue more large then they;
By all thy brim-fill'd Bowles of feirce desire,
By thy last Morning's draught of liquid fire;
By the full kingdome of that finall kisse
That seiz'd thy parting Soul, & seal'd thee his;
By all the heau'ns thou hast in him
(Fair sister of the SERAPHIM!)
By all of HIM we haue in THEE;
Leaue nothing of my SELF in me.
Let me so read thy life, that I
Vnto all life of mine may dy.[1]

[1] *The Flaming Heart upon the Book and Picture of the seraphicall saint Teresa.*

CHAPTER VII

ANDREW MARVELL, 1621–1678

ANDREW MARVELL was almost the exact contemporary of Henry Vaughan, born one year earlier and, like Vaughan, writing his best lyrical poetry in the early 1650's. Both poets would be included today in any anthology of seventeenth-century metaphysical poetry, and each would also probably be represented in an anthology of English nature poetry. And yet as soon as one reads their poems one is struck by the difference in their form, style, tone and content. This will be at once obvious if we juxtapose with almost any devotional poem by Vaughan, Marvell's *On a Drop of Dew*, a devotional poem depending on nature-imagery and to that extent comparable with, for instance, *The Morning-watch*.

On a Drop of Dew

See how the Orient Dew,
Shed from the Bosom of the Morn
  Into the blowing Roses,
Yet careless of its Mansion new;
For the clear Region where 'twas born
  Round in its self incloses:
  And in its little Globes Extent,
Frames as it can its native Element.
  How it the purple flow'r does slight,
  Scarce touching where it lyes,
  But gazing back upon the Skies,
  Shines with a mournful Light;
    Like its own Tear,
Because so long divided from the Sphear.
  Restless it roules and unsecure,
  Trembling lest it grow impure:
  Till the warm Sun pitty it's Pain,
And to the Skies exhale it back again.
  So the Soul, that Drop, that Ray

> Of the clear Fountain of Eternal Day,
> Could it within the humane flow'r be seen,
>   Remembring still its former height,
>   Shuns the sweat leaves and blossoms green;
>   And, recollecting its own Light,
> Does, in its pure and circling thoughts, express
> The greater Heaven in an Heaven less.
>   In how coy a Figure wound,
>   Every way it turns away:
>   So the World excluding round,
>   Yet receiving in the Day.
>   Dark beneath, but bright above:
>   Here disdaining, there in Love.
>   How loose and easie hence to go:
>   How girt and ready to ascend.
>   Moving but on a point below,
>   It all about does upwards bend.
> Such did the Manna's sacred Dew destil;
> White, and intire, though congeal'd and chill.
> Congeal'd on Earth: but does, dissolving, run
> Into the Glories of th'Almighty Sun.

The logical structure of the poem suggests the Donne tradition whereas logical structure is the aspect of metaphysical style that is least evident in Vaughan's poetry. Marvell 'applies' the dew-drop to the Christian soul as, in geometry, one triangle can be 'applied' to another and found by a process of reasoning to be exactly congruent with it. The intellectual pleasure of perceiving this identity between dew-drop and soul is a basic element in the delight the poem affords. In the first eighteen lines Marvell elaborates this relation so that in the next eighteen lines he can 'prove' that the dew-drop in the flower is an exact emblem of the soul in the body; the 'Orient Dew' cares little for its new 'Mansion' because it mirrors the heaven from which it comes; if it resembles a tear that is because it mourns for its native element; it is restless and anxious lest it lose its purity; the sun draws it back into 'the clear Region where 'twas born'. In the next line the identity with the human soul is stated and then, in the same number of lines as it took him to describe the dew-drop in its relation to the rose, Marvell describes the relation of the soul to the body. The total argument of the poem is that the soul cannot be satisfied in the body; it does not find rest on earth any more than the morning's dew-drop finds a final resting-place in the rose (though the earth and the rose are lovely). In the last four lines of the poem Marvell adds the comparison with another kind of dew, the heaven-sent manna described in Exodus xvi. 14 as 'a small round thing, as small as the hoar-frost on the ground', or, as the poet describes it:

> White, and intire, though congeal'd and chill

and again the parallel is full and rich in its implication; the manna, like the dew and like the soul, comes from Heaven. As the dew 'trembles lest it grow impure', so is the manna 'congealed and chill' on earth and all three, dew, soul and manna aspire to

> run
> Into the Glories of th'Almighty Sun.

In another poem called *A Dialogue between the Soul and Body* Marvell treats the soul, not this time as a transient inmate of the body, but as an uneasy partner. Again this could be described as a poem in the Donne tradition; it makes the same kind of demand on the reader as Donne's poems do, the demand to follow and enjoy an argument. It assumes as do all the 'metaphysical' poems of the seventeenth century the basic conception that man is

> A little world made cunningly
> Of Elements, and an Angelicke spright.

And again it is as unlike any poem by Donne or Vaughan or Herbert as, say, Keats's *Ode to Autumn* is unlike any poem by Wordsworth, Shelley or Byron. To know the movement of thought and the conventions of style within which a poet wrote is an aid to appreciation. Yet the better the poet is, the more certainly will his poem bear the stamp of his own individuality. In the four stanzas of Marvell's poem the soul and the body alternately accuse each other of causing acute distress.

A Dialogue between the Soul and Body

Soul

O who shall, from this Dungeon, raise
A Soul inslav'd so many wayes?
With bolts of Bones, that fetter'd stands
In Feet; and manacled in Hands.
Here blinded with an Eye; and there
Deaf with the drumming of an Ear.
A Soul hung up, as 'twere, in Chains
Of Nerves, and Arteries, and Veins.
Tortur'd, besides each other part,
In a vain Head, and double Heart.

Body

O who shall me deliver whole,
From bonds of this Tyrannic Soul?
Which, stretcht upright, impales me so,
That mine own Precipice I go;
And warms and moves this needless Frame:
(A Fever could but do the same.)
And, wanting where its spight to try,
Has made me live to let me dye.
A Body that could never rest,
Since this ill Spirit it possest.

Soul

What Magick could me thus confine
Within anothers Grief to pine?
Where whatsoever it complain,
I feel, that cannot feel, the pain.
And all my Care its self employes,
That to preserve, which me destroys:
Constrain'd not only to indure
Diseases, but, whats worse, the Cure:
And ready oft the Port to gain,
Am Shipwrackt into Health again.

Body

But Physick yet could never reach
The Maladies Thou me dost teach;
Whom first the Cramp of Hope does Tear:
And then the Palsie Shakes of Fear.
The Pestilence of Love does heat:
Or Hatred's hidden Ulcer eat.
Joy's chearful Madness does perplex:
Or Sorrow's other Madness vex.
Which Knowledge forces me to know;
And Memory will not foregoe.
What but a Soul could have the wit
To build me up for Sin so fit?
So Architects do square and hew,
Green Trees that in the Forest grew.

The conception of soul and body fused together and thus giving to man his unique place in the hierarchy of being was familiar to all Marvell's contemporary readers; we are aware of it in other 'metaphysical' poems. But what Marvell here makes of that conception is new and is characteristic of him. The effect of the poem depends in part on the witty precision of the images, especially on the amusing and arresting appropriateness of the tortures inflicted by the body on the soul and by the soul on the body. Each stanza is witty, or what we should call clever, in the unexpected but valid additions it makes to the theme. But this is much more than a 'clever' poem; it records an insight into human experience. The poem throws light on the predicament of man, suffering as no other creature suffers, just because he is higher in the scale of being: animals are at peace, only man has

A Body that could never rest,
Since this ill Spirit it possest.

But, conversely, the soul suffers as angels do not, because, unlike other spiritual beings, man's soul is incarnate and

Constrain'd not only to indure
Diseases, but, whats worse, the Cure.

It is not easy for the soul as it is for a drop of dew to return to 'the clear Region where 'twas born'. Without any elaboration or any comment direct from the poet, keeping strictly within the framework of a dialectic argument between his two personae, Marvell spotlights the predicament of man; he allows the last word and the fullest statement of that predicament to the body. The soul's capacity to hope, to fear, to love, to hate, to know, to remember, are the causes of sin. No other creature except man can sin, since no other creature has a soul yoked with its body. What the soul does is to transform man's nature and Marvell suggests a parallel with the artificer who transforms nature into art, for instance the gardener's topiary art:

> So Architects do square and hew,
> Green Trees that in the Forest grew.

The simile is richer and more apt than a hasty reading suggests. Almost always in Marvell's poetry 'green', which is a favourite adjective, evokes the idea of Paradise and of innocence before the Fall. The body's complaint is that the soul caused it to know good and evil and to be capable of sin, as other creatures are not.

Mr T. S. Eliot, in an essay on Marvell first published in 1921, defined seventeenth-century wit as 'a tough reasonableness beneath the slight lyric grace', and the phrase is especially suggestive of the quality of Marvell's poetry. The 'slight lyric grace' in his handling of language and metre gives his poems a deceptive air of simplicity: no one would miss the tough reasonableness in Donne's poems, the metre and the language invite the reader to grapple with it. But the more intimately one comes to know Marvell's poems the more appropriate it seems to stress 'tough reasonableness' in them too. He delights as much as Donne does in all the uses to which logical argument can be put, including 'proof' of the absurd or paradoxical. He is also a poet of 'tough reasonableness' in another sense, as we say that a man is 'reasonable' when he is aware of the world or has his feet on the ground. The green innocent natural world in Marvell's nature poetry is seen by one who is keenly aware of the world inhabited by fallen man.

The Garden is the most sustained and complex of Marvell's nature poems and it illustrates his distinctive characteristics. It has his customary 'lyric grace' which relates to his almost exclusive use of the four-foot, rhyming, iambic couplet; the measure is fluid and immediately pleasing to the ear. Donne's brilliant use of metre at once suggests complexity of thought and feeling: sometimes the reader needs to discover the grammatical sense before he can know how much stress to give to a word—for the metrical stress and the meaning stress may not coincide. Conversely a reader may arrive at the meaning only because his ear informed him how the lines ought to sound. But in Marvell's poetry metre and sentence structure move in graceful partnership; there is a deceptive air of simplicity, we catch the tune so easily. But the poems are not simple and delight often springs from the contrast between the song-like flow of the verse and the paradoxical or ambiguous implications of the language. *The Garden* opens with a conceit opposing the plants that symbolize fame to those that grow in gardens:

I

How vainly men themselves amaze
To win the Palm, the Oke, or Bayes;
And their uncessant Labours see
Crown'd from some single Herb or Tree.
Whose short and narrow verged Shade
Does prudently their Toyles upbraid;
While all Flow'rs and all Trees do close
To weave the Garlands of repose.

Even Marvell's use of metre is not as simple as it at first seems; the variant in the penultimate line suggests the rich abundance of those garlands, and the placing of 'uncessant' astride the second and third foot in line three causes the rhythm to mirror the meaning. Metrical analysis could no doubt demonstrate Marvell's subtle command of his apparently simple metre, but the reader's ear responds readily enough without it. The pun on the word 'upbraid' is in keeping with the tone of the stanza; a tone which is not solemn but amused; a victor's crown is braided-up (as a girl braids up her hair), it is a woven crown, whether it be the civic crown made of oak leaves or the hero's crown of palm, or the poet's of bay. But upbraid (reproach) is also implied; their toil is reproached by the very garland they coveted. What folly it is to prefer the scanty protection of a leafy crown to the shade of a garden where all the flowers and trees weave the garland. This announces the theme of the poem and the second stanza expands the contrast and relates it to the predicament of man.

II

> Fair quiet, have I found thee here,
> And Innocence thy Sister dear!
> Mistaken long, I sought you then
> In busie Companies of Men.
> Your sacred Plants, if here below,
> Only among the Plants will grow.
> Society is all but rude,
> To this delicious Solitude.

A modern reader might miss the paradox of the last couplet which would probably have been the most pungent effect of the stanza for a seventeenth-century reader. It seems natural for us post-romantics to think of society as rude compared with a man alone in a garden. But in the seventeenth century the word society implied the opposite of 'rudeness'; it implied the virtues upon which civilization depends. 'Association with one's fellow men in a friendly or intimate manner' is the Oxford Dictionary's definition. The first illustrative quotation given there is from Elyot's *The Governour*, 1531: 'Society, without which man's life is

unpleasant and full of anguish.' When Marvell asserts that
society is 'almost rude' by comparison with 'this delicious
solitude' it ought to give the reader a shock; but he will of
course also remember that there once was 'Innocence' in
a Garden. There was innocence, but not solitude: the poem
will return to this point. Meanwhile, Marvell introduces
another goal men have pursued, besides personal glory; he
reminds the reader of the tradition of courtly love and of all
the poets who have celebrated fair ladies whose 'cheeks are
rose and lilly':

III

No white nor red was ever seen
So am'rous as this lovely green.
Fond Lovers, cruel as their Flame,
Cut in these Trees their Mistress name.
Little, Alas, they know, or heed,
How far these Beauties Hers exceed!
Fair Trees! Where s'eer your barkes I wound,
No Name shall but your own be found.

And then, still relying on his reader's familiarity with
literary tradition, he reverses the meaning of those *Meta-
morphoses* sung by Ovid, wherein fair ladies, chased by
amorous gods, are transformed into trees:

IV

When we have run our Passion's heat,
Love hither makes his best retreat.
The *Gods*, that mortal Beauty chase,
Still in a Tree did end their race.
Apollo hunted *Daphne* so,
Only that She might Laurel grow.
And *Pan* did after *Syrinx* speed,
Not as a Nymph, but for a Reed.

In the next stanza there is a characteristic modulation of
tone from gay, witty, paradoxical assertions of the garden's
supremacy to rich hyperbolical description of its delights:

V

What wond'rous Life in this I lead!
Ripe Apples drop about my head;
The Luscious Clusters of the Vine
Upon my Mouth do crush their Wine;
The Nectaren, and curious Peach,
Into my hands themselves do reach;
Stumbling on Melons, as I pass,
Insnar'd with Flow'rs, I fall on Grass.

The garden itself has become the wooer: apples 'drop' on his head, grapes 'crush' their wine on his mouth; the adjective 'curious' used of the peach implies not only that it is 'exquisite' but that it is 'importunately inquiring'. Melons make him stumble, flowers ensnare him—the whole garden is in active pursuit, and he falls softly 'on grass'.

This rich sensuousness leads into another modulation of tone in the next stanzas where the poem moves to its climax and speaks of the mind in the act of contemplation; the tempo changes, we read more slowly as befits the substance of the next two stanzas.

VI

Meanwhile the Mind, from pleasure less,
Withdraws into its happiness:
The Mind, that Ocean where each kind
Does streight its own resemblance find;
Yet it creates, transcending these,
Far other Worlds, and other Seas;
Annihilating all that's made
To a green Thought in a green Shade.

Professor Empson (in *Some Versions of Pastoral*) detects two main ambiguities, or puns, in the stanzas, one of which seems to enrich the meaning and is therefore likely to have been intended by the poet; the other seems to contradict the meaning and to be, therefore, inadmissible. The first ambiguity is in the phrase 'from pleasure less' which can grammatically mean both *the mind withdraws from the lesser pleasures of worldly life* and *the mind, diminished by pleasure*, *now withdraws into its true happiness.* Both meanings are consonant with the total sense of the stanza. The second ambiguity suggested is that 'Does streight its own resemblance find' means both *does straightaway find* and *does find straightened or narrowed.* The second is, in my view, unacceptable because it conflicts with the total effect of magnifying the mind. The mind is an ocean which (as was believed of the real ocean) contains within it a replica of all the creatures. But the mind does even more than the ocean, it not only reproduces, but creates. It is capable of annihilating all that's made and doing what Coleridge was later to define as the work of the secondary imagination, which 'dissolves, diffuses, dissipates in order to recreate'.

When Marvell speaks of the mind

> Annihilating all that's made
> To a green Thought in a green Shade,

he again suggests that the garden can lead back to the Garden of Eden and pristine innocence. He describes the escape of the soul from the body in the act of contemplation.

VII

> Here at the Fountains sliding foot,
> Or at some Fruit-trees mossy root,
> Casting the Bodies Vest aside,
> My Soul into the boughs does glide:
> There like a Bird it sits, and sings,
> Then whets, and combs its silver Wings;
> And, till prepar'd for longer flight,
> Waves in its Plumes the various Light.

These two stanzas, VI and VII, are the climax of the poem to which all that precedes them leads. We are to reject fame, courtly love and all that men seek in 'busie Companies of Men', because it is in the solitude and peace of the garden that the soul can best prepare itself for heaven. It is the climax, but it is not the end of Marvell's poem. He is too much aware of the world and of the realities of man's fallen state to think of the enjoyment of the garden's beauty and the contemplation of eternity as a permanent refuge. The garden is a temporary retreat, reminiscent of paradise: in stanza VIII he reminds us of what happened there:

VIII

Such was that happy Garden-state,
While Man there walk'd without a Mate:
After a Place so pure, and sweet,
What other Help could yet be meet!
But 'twas beyond a Mortal's share
To wander solitary there:
Two Paradises 'twere in one
To live in Paradise alone.

There is a note of sardonic amusement in the reference to Eve. The last stanza of the poem brings us back to the actual garden that inspired the poem, the garden at Appleton House:

IX

How well the skilful Gardner drew
Of flow'rs and herbes this Dial new;
Where from above the milder Sun
Does through a fragrant Zodiack run;
And, as it works, th' industrious Bee
Computes its time as well as we.
How could such sweet and wholesome Hours
Be reckon'd but with herbs and flow'rs!

Hours spent in a garden, freed from the pressure of time, can be measured by a dial made of herbs wherein the industrious bee counts the time (with a pun on *thyme* which is more explicit in Marvell's Latin version of the poem). And the bee too reminds us that we live in a work-a-day world.

Marvell again celebrated the formalized beauty of the garden at Nun Appleton in his poem *Upon Appleton House*; he lived there as tutor to General Fairfax's daughter between 1650 and 1653. It was a temporary retreat from the world. Afterwards he offered his services to Cromwell

and became for a time tutor to Cromwell's ward, William
Dutton. In 1657 he was appointed as Latin Secretary to the
Parliament and became the colleague of Milton, who had
recommended him. After Cromwell's death, in Richard
Cromwell's reign, Marvell was member for Hull and he was
re-elected in April 1660 immediately before the Restoration,
and, for a third term, a year later, in the reign of Charles II.
He wrote three poems concerning Cromwell: the great
Horation Ode on Cromwell's Return from Ireland (1650),
The First Anniversary of the Government under O.C. and
A Poem upon the Death of O.C. During the reign of
Charles II, Marvell was writing anonymous political satires.
He was always aware of, and was often a participator in,
the political events of the age. In *Upon Appleton House*,
amidst the elaborate and fanciful descriptions of the house
and garden there is a moving passage on the Civil War. In
the garden at Nun Appleton, so Fairfax's biographer tells
us, 'the flowers were planted in masses, tulips, pinks and
roses each in separate beds, which were cut into the shape
of forts with five bastions'. This horticultural fantasy is
Marvell's basis for the famous passage from stanza XLI to
XLV. At the close of the thirty-ninth stanza he describes the
effect:

> See how the Flow'rs, as at *Parade*,
> Under their *Colours* stand displaid:
> Each *Regiment* in order grows,
> That of the Tulip Pinke and Rose.

> XL

> But when the vigilant *Patroul*
> Of Stars walks round about the *Pole*,
> Their Leaves, that to the stalks are curl'd,
> Seem to their Staves the *Ensigns* furl'd.
> Then in some Flow'rs beloved Hut
> Each Bee as Sentinel is shut;
> And sleeps so too: but, if once stir'd,
> She runs you through, or askes *the Word*.

So far Marvell has done little more than translate into words the amusing analogy devised by General Fairfax; but in the next stanza a graver note is sounded:

XLI

Oh Thou, that dear and happy Isle
The Garden of the World ere while,
Thou *Paradise* of the four Seas,
Which *Heaven* planted us to please,
But, to exclude the World, did guard
With watry if not flaming Sword;
What luckless Apple did we tast,
To make us Mortal, and The Wast?

XLII

Unhappy! shall we never more
That sweet *Militia* restore,
When Gardens only had their Tow'rs,
And all the Garrisons were Flow'rs,
When Roses only Arms might bear,
And Men did rosie Garlands wear?
Tulips, in several Colours barr'd,
Were then the *Switzers* of our *Guard*.

XLIII

The *Gardiner* had the *Souldiers* place,
And his more gentle Forts did trace.
The Nursery of all things green
Was then the only *Magazeen*.
The *Winter Quarters* were the Stoves,
Where he the tender Plants removes.
But War all this doth overgrow:
We Ordnance Plant and Powder sow.

and in the next two stanzas, which end the direct reference to the state of civil war, Marvell comments on Fairfax's withdrawal from his command. He had resigned in 1650 rather than attack Scotland, saying: 'Human probabilities are not sufficient to make war upon a neighbour nation, especially our brethren of Scotland, to whom we are engaged in a solemn league and covenant.' Fairfax had also been opposed to the execution of Charles, and his position as General of the army must since then have tormented his conscience. Marvell, in the two following stanzas, conveys first his regret that Fairfax can no longer serve the country, and then his recognition of those scruples which caused him to withdraw.

XLIV

And yet there walks one on the Sod
Who, had it pleased him and *God,*
Might once have made our Gardens spring
Fresh as his own and flourishing.
But he preferr'd to the *Cinque Ports*
These five imaginary Forts;
And, in those half-dry Trenches, spann'd
Pow'r which the Ocean might command.

XLV

For he did, with his utmost Skill,
Ambition weed, but *Conscience* till.
Conscience, that Heaven-nursed Plant,
Which most our Earthly Gardens want.
A prickling leaf it bears, and such
As that which shrinks at ev'ry touch;
But Flow'rs eternal, and divine,
That in the crowns of Saints do shine.

Marvell's political consciousness accounts for some of the differences between his poems and those of Vaughan or Herbert. Contemplation of nature and Christian theology in Marvell's lyrical poetry are closely related to his awareness of the state of England. This is part of his particular brand of 'tough reasonableness'.

Perhaps two of Marvell's love poems, *The Definition of Love* and *To his Coy Mistress,* show him most obviously as a poet in the metaphysical tradition. Each is an argument, pressing towards a conclusion by seemingly logical steps. In the first, logic and play with ambiguities in the language lead to the conclusion that fatally separated lovers are, by definition, superior to happier pairs:

As Lines so Loves *oblique* may well
Themselves in every Angle greet:

123   5-2

> But ours so truly *Paralel*,
> Though infinite can never meet.

The geometric images of triangle and parallel lines is made, by word play, to suggest a contrast between clandestine lovers meeting in corners and a 'marriage of true minds'; 'infinite' and 'oblique' do double duty so that the conclusion appears to be logical:

> Therefore the Love which us doth bind,
> But Fate so enviously debarrs,
> Is the Conjunction of the Mind,
> And Opposition of the Stars.

It is an image comparable with Donne's compass image in *A Valediction: Forbidding Mourning*; but it is (to use Coleridge's terminology) fanciful where Donne's is imaginative. Only linguistic accident enables Marvell to get the effect he wants. Donne's image gathers up and concentrates the idea and emotion that precedes it—the idea that parting is not separation and that the union with his beloved both perfects his action ('draws my circle just') and ensures his return ('makes me end where I begun'). Another difference between *The Definition* and most of Donne's love poems is the absence of dramatic tension; Donne's poems imply the presence of the mistress whom the lover comforts, or with whom he pleads. Marvell in this poem is, as the title implies, defining the situation; consequently he distances it and expresses it in abstract terms. Only in the first two stanzas does he convey feeling:

> My Love is of a birth so rare
> As 'tis for object strange and high:
> It was begotten by despair
> Upon Impossibility.
>
> Magnanimous Despair alone
> Could show me so divine a thing,
> Where feeble Hope could ne'r have flown
> But vainly flapt its Tinsel Wing.

But in *To his Coy Mistress* Marvell writes a dramatic poem, and achieves one of the supreme lyrics on the recurrent theme 'gather the rosebud while ye may'. He builds his poem in three phases, each representing a step in the argument: first the supposition, then the necessity to reject it, and lastly the consequence of rejecting it. I call it a 'dramatic' poem because we imagine the woman as present and because of the mounting tension. The poem opens with a slow movement, a series of hyperboles in praise of the lady, describing what he would do *if* human life were not bounded by space and time.

> Had we but World enough, and Time,
> This coyness Lady were no crime.
> We would sit down, and think which way
> To walk, and pass our long Loves Day.
> Thou by the *Indian Ganges* side
> Should'st Rubies find; I by the Tide
> Of *Humber* would complain. I would
> Love you ten years before the Flood:
> And you should if you please refuse
> Till the Conversion of the *Jews*.
> My vegetable Love should grow
> Vaster than Empires, and more slow.
> An hundred years should go to praise
> Thine Eyes, and on thy Forehead Gaze.
> Two hundred to adore each Breast:
> But thirty thousand to the rest.
> An Age at least to every part,
> And the last Age should show your Heart.
> For Lady you deserve this State;
> Nor would I love at lower rate.

In the next movement the pace accelerates; the poet has told his lady what he would do *if.* Now follows the *but* and it requires no play on words; human experience itself makes the logical sequence compelling:

> But at my back I alwaies hear
> Times winged Charriot hurrying near:
> And yonder all before us lye

> Desarts of vast Eternity.
> Thy Beauty shall no more be found;
> Nor, in thy marble Vault shall sound
> My ecchoing Song: then Worms shall try
> That long preserv'd Virginity:
> And your quaint Honour turn to dust;
> And into ashes all my *Lust*.

And, instead of the courtly couplet that closes the first movement, this ends with the frightening, haste-compelling, sardonic couplet:

> The Grave's a fine and private place,
> But none I think do there embrace.

First the elaborate supposition governed by *if*, then the urgent recognition of reality governed by *but* and finally the passionate and logical conclusion,

> Now therefore, while the youthful hew
> Sits on thy skin like morning lew,
> And while thy willing Soul transpires
> At every pore with instant Fires,
> Now let us sport us while we may;
> And now, like am'rous birds of prey,
> Rather at once our Time devour,
> Than languish in his slow-chapt pow'r.
> Let us roll all our Strength, and all
> Our sweetness, up into one Ball:
> And tear our Pleasures with rough strife,
> Thorough the Iron gates of Life.
> Thus, though we cannot make our Sun
> Stand still, yet we will make him run.

So the poem comes full circle, the enemy time is discovered, feared and—in the only way appropriate to the theme—conquered.

All the poems so far quoted were almost certainly written while Marvell was at Nun Appleton, that is to say between the early summer of 1651 and the same season in 1653. It was during these three years of rural retreat that Marvell's lyrical genius flowered. Later he was to become a political satirist. But before he went to Nun Appleton he wrote a great public ode, the *Ode upon Cromwel's return from Ireland*. Cromwell returned from his military victory there in May 1650. Professor Margoliouth, editor of the Clarendon Press edition of Marvell's Poems and Letters, thinks it probable that Marvell did not know Fairfax personally at that time so that, in so far as the ideas in the poem resemble Fairfax's, this is evidence of like-mindedness, not of direct influence. Cromwell too was at this time personally unknown to Marvell; the two later poems, *The First Anniversary of the Government under O.C.* (1655) and *A Poem upon the Death of O.C.* (1658), show increasing respect and, in the last, personal grief. But in the *Ode* Cromwell is the public character, seen and judged and warned by a clear-sighted observer who is also a masterly poet, acquainted with the classical works in this kind, especially the odes of Horace and Lucan's *Pharsalia*. On the surface the poem is a panegyric on the Lord Lieutenant of Ireland, the Commander-in-Chief of the army; Cromwell was given the command when Fairfax refused it and resigned for reasons of conscience. Cromwell's next assignment was the attack on Scotland that Fairfax would not undertake. The note of triumph sounds in the metre (which Marvell used only for this poem):

> The forward Youth that would appear
> Must now forsake his *Muses* dear,
>   Nor in the Shadows sing
>   His Numbers languishing.
> 'Tis time to leave the Books in dust,
> And oyl th'unused Armour's rust:
>   Removing from the Wall
>   The Corslet of the Hall.

But, after sounding this warlike note and giving the rhythm which will ring throughout the poem, he introduces the hero with judicial insight:

> So restless *Cromwel* could not cease
> In the inglorious Arts of Peace,

> But through adventrous War
> Urged his active Star.
> And, like the three-forked Lightning, first
> Breaking the Clouds where it was nurst,
> Did thorough his own Side
> His fiery way divide.

The images of the lightning bursting through the cloud, with its suggestion that the cloud was the nurse of the lightning and that, to reach eminence, Cromwell had to do violence even to his supporters, is continued as the metaphor is extended:

> For 'tis all one to Courage high
> The Emulous or Enemy;
> And with such to inclose
> Is more than to oppose.
> Then burning through the Air he went,
> And Pallaces and Temples rent:
> And *Caesars* head at last
> Did through his Laurels blast.

But the metaphor serves also to enforce the idea of inevitability and of Cromwell as a man fated to do the work of violence. This leads into a passage of sympathy for Cromwell, as the willing tool of destiny:

> 'Tis Madness to resist or blame
> The force of angry Heavens flame:
> And, if we would speak true,
> Much to the man is due.
> Who from his private Gardens, where
> He liv'd reserved and austere,
> As if his highest plot
> To plant the Bergamot,
> Could by industrious Valour climbe
> To ruine the great Work of Time,
> And cast the Kingdome old
> Into another Mold.

The lines have a deliberate ambiguity which runs through the whole poem. On the one hand we are aware of revolution and regicide as necessary, and of Cromwell as a man

who has forsaken his own peace to do the work that had
to be done; on the other hand, and mainly here by the
choice of one verb 'ruined', the note of censure is sounded.
Similarly in the next couplet the Fate of which Cromwell is
the instrument is opposed to 'Justice', but then again, by
means of a metaphysical image, Marvell reaffirms the inevitability:

> Though Justice against Fate complain,
> And plead the Antient Rights in vain:
>> But those do hold or break
>> As Men are strong or weak.
> Nature that hateth emptiness,
> Allows of penetration less:
>> And therefore must make room
>> Where greater Spirits come.
> What field of all the Civil Wars
> Where his were not the deepest Scars?

Cromwell did, heroically, what he had to do. But in the
next six lines Marvell charges the hero with a cruel cunning:

> And *Hampton* shows what part
> He had of wiser Art.
> Where, twining subtile fears with hope,
> He wove a net of such a scope,
>> That *Charles* himself might chase
>> To *Careisbrooks* narrow case.

History has exonerated Cromwell from the charge of
deliberately luring Charles from Hampton Court to
Carisbrooke Castle, but Marvell is accepting a contemporary belief to the discredit of his hero. His is no ordinary
song of praise. This notion of what Lilburne called a
'mouse-trap' set by Cromwell to catch the king is the
prelude to Marvell's famous account of the execution.
Charles was lured to Carisbrooke:

> That thence the *Royal Actor* born
> The *Tragick Scaffold* might adorn:
>> While round the armed Bands
>> Did clap their bloody hands.

The metaphor of the theatre reinforces the idea of Charles bearing his part in the tragedy, accepting his fate with the nobility of a Greek tragic hero:

> *He* nothing common did or mean
> Upon that memorable Scene:
> But with his keener Eye
> The Axes edge did try:
> Nor call'd the *Gods* with vulgar spight
> To vindicate his helpless Right,
> But bow'd his comely Head
> Down as upon a Bed.
> This was that memorable Hour
> Which first assur'd the forced Pow'r.

And Marvell associates that inauguration of power with the founding of Rome and, in particular, with the legend that when the foundations were dug a bleeding human head was found and was thought to be of good augury. Marvell's introduction of this bleeding head is, again, ambiguous:

> So when they did design
> The *Capitols* first Line,
> A bleeding Head where they begun,
> Did fright the Architects to run;
> And yet in that the *State*
> Foresaw it's happy Fate.

The bleeding head of Charles I, whose death the poem has already associated with that of tragic heroes, may *yet* augur the happy fate of England. It is in that context of dismay and doubt and hope that Marvell goes on to celebrate Cromwell's victory in Ireland, the actual occasion of the ode. Ireland has been 'in one Year tam'd', the Irish 'affirm his praises' because he has been 'good and just'. There are grounds for this assertion; Cromwell was able to challenge the Catholic clergy to 'Give us an instance of one man, since my coming into Ireland, not in arms, massacred, destroyed, or banished, concerning the massacre of whom justice has not been done or endeavoured to be done'. Nevertheless, as the poem goes on to assert, the bloody victory in Ireland is only a prelude to further fighting. Cromwell may wish now for peace:

> So when the Falcon high
> Falls heavy from the Sky
> She, having kill'd, no more does search,
> But on the next green Bow to pearch;
> Where, when he first does lure,
> The Falckner has her sure.
> What may not then our *Isle* presume
> While Victory his Crest does plume!
> What may not others fear
> If thus he crown each Year!

The image of the Falcon is a warning and a spur; Cromwell must proceed to further conquests so that he may be feared abroad:

> A Caesar he ere long to *Gaul*,
> To *Italy* an *Hannibal*,
> And to all States not free
> Shall *Clymacterick* be.

and the immediate task at hand is the one Fairfax had refused:

> The *Pict* no shelter now shall find
> Within his parti-colour'd Mind;
> But from his Valour sad
> Shrink underneath the Plad:
> Happy if in the tufted brake
> The English Hunter him mistake;
> Nor lay his Hounds in near
> The *Caledonian* Deer.

It does not seem as though Marvell at this time shared Fairfax's view of the attack on Scotland, and the lines quoted earlier from *Upon Appleton House* suggest that he continued to doubt, although he respected the conscience-scruple. In the *Horatian Ode* at any rate Marvell sees the hero, Cromwell, as one doomed to rule by fear and force. So the poem ends with a martial and a warning note:

But thou the Wars and Fortune's Son
March indefatigably on;
    And for the last effect
    Still keep the Sword erect:
Besides the force it has to fright
The Spirits of the Shady Night,
    The same *Arts* that did *gain*
    A *Pow'r* must it *maintain*.

In this great occasional poem there is again 'tough reasonableness' as well as 'lyric grace'. The verse sings; its tune is appropriate to a triumphal ode. But the meaning is fuller and more complex than mere triumph; it includes critical judgment. Marvell suggests flaws of character that fit Cromwell for his destiny; he recognizes the harshness of that destiny and the 'ruin' involved in it; he also recognizes Cromwell's virtues and he indicates further consequences of the part Cromwell has chosen, and been chosen to play.

The clear judgment combined with strong feeling in the *Ode* relates it to the Donne tradition, and the way the images are developed as arguments by analogy is a mark of the metaphysical style. Yet to claim that Marvell is a metaphysical poet is to conform to a fairly recent critical fashion. When in 1905 Augustine Birrell wrote a book about Marvell for the *English Men of Letters* series, no such affiliation occurred to him. Instead, he declared that in Marvell's lyrical poems 'may be heard for the last time the priceless note of the Elizabethan lyrist, whilst at the same time utterance is being given to feelings which reach far forward to Wordsworth and Shelley'. Perhaps the modern critic overlooks qualities that Birrell points to here. There is an Elizabethan grace and freshness in Marvell's verse and the tradition of courtly love is there, for instance in *The Picture of little T.C. in a Prospect of Flowers*, while its presence in the reader's mind is assumed in *The Garden*. The 'feelings reaching far forward' are, presumably, feelings about nature, although I suspect the resemblance to Wordsworth's feelings or Shelley's is not close. More certainly there are recordings of visual perceptions, sights noticed with delight and accurately rendered, for example the birds Marvell saw when he carelessly trod on a strawberry bed (in *Upon Appleton House*):

> Then as I carless on the Bed
> Of gelid *Straw-berryes* do tread,
> And through the Hazels thick espy
> The hatching *Thrastles* shining Eye,
> The *heron* from the Ashes top,
> The eldest of its young lets drop,...

And there is Marvell's delight in colour; the lily-white fawn among the roses in *The Nymph Complaining of the Death of her Fawn*, or the oranges in the green grove in *Bermudas*:

> He hangs in shades the Orange bright,
> Like golden Lamps in a green Night.

These moments are more Keats-like than anything in Donne, Herbert or even Vaughan. Nevertheless, Marvell's poetry has only a tenuous resemblance either to the Elizabethans or the Romantics. It is more searching and intellectual than most Elizabethan lyrics, and it is more worldly-wise and witty than most romantic poetry. It is best, I think, to read him alongside his immediate predecessors and his contemporaries, adding if we can the Latin poets whom he loved and imitated. All these formed the tradition in which he wrote. But in his essay *Tradition and the Individual Talent*, Mr Eliot reminded us that 'to conform merely would not really be to conform at all; it would not be new, it would not therefore be a work of art'. And, even from the small selection from Marvell's poems discussed here, it should be clear that Marvell is a true poet, not conforming to any tradition but making use of several to write poems that are unmistakably new and his own.

CHAPTER VIII

RELIGIOUS POETRY:
A POSTSCRIPT

Contemplative piety, or the intercourse between God and the human soul, cannot be poetical.

DR JOHNSON, *Life of Waller*

THE poets to whom Donne's influence was most congenial were religious poets. Conceits reminiscent of his and poems influenced by his conception of structure and rhythm are common in the love poetry of the day; but, when one examines them more closely, the likeness to Donne proves often to be superficial:

Excuse of Absence.

You will not ask, perhaps, wherefore I stay,
Loving so much, so long away—
O do not think 'twas I did part,
It was my body, not my heart;
For, like a compass, on your love
One foot is fix'd, and cannot move:
Th'other may follow the blind guide
Of giddy Fortune, but not slide
    Beyond your service, nor dare venter
    To wander far from you, the centre.

The very closeness with which Carew has imitated here makes it easy to point to the difference. Donne's figure of the compass, in *A Valediction: forbidding mourning*, is more profound than Carew's adaptation of it. Its neat aptitude may be the first thing that strikes a reader; but he is soon carried beyond mere pleasure in a pretty fancy:

Thy soule the fixt foot, makes no show
    To move, but doth, if the 'other doe.

And though it in the center sit,
    Yet when the other far doth rome,
It leanes, and hearkens after it,
    And growes erect, as that comes home.

Such words as 'rome', 'leanes', 'hearkens' gather up emotion into the intellectual image. It seems, as so often in Donne's poems, that one law is at work in all experience. The same flame that lights the intellect warms the heart; mathematics and love obey one principle. The binding of a circle and the union of lovers are equivalent symbols of eternity and perfection:

Thy firmnes draws my circle just,
    And makes me end, where I begunne.[1]

Donne's images constantly imply that all phenomena are facets of a single whole. The following extracts illustrate this:

But since my soule, whose child love is,
Takes limmes of flesh, and else could nothing doe,
    More subtile then the parent is,
Love must not be, but take a body too.
                                Aire and Angels

But as all severall soules containe
    Mixture of things, they know not what,
Love, these mixed soules, doth mixe againe,
    And makes both one, each this and that.
A single violet transplant,
    The strength, the colour, and the size,
(All which before was poore and scant,)
    Redoubles still, and multiplies.

When love, with one another so
    Interinanimates two soules,
That abler soule, which thence doth flow,
    Defects of lonelinesse controules.   *The Extasie*

[1] The fixed foot of the compass leans towards the other while the circle is being described. When that is completed the outstretched foot is brought back to the other (the compasses are closed up). While the circle is being described the 'firmness' with which the fixed foot is pinned in the centre is what makes the circle 'just'. My excuse for explaining this figure is that some modern critics have obscured its meaning in their search for ambiguities.

If, as in water stir'd more circles bee
Produc'd by one, love such additions take,
Those like so many spheares, but one heaven make,
For, they are all concentrique unto thee.

Loves growth.

All poetic images derive from a perception of relation, but
not all lay such stress on an underlying principle of unity.
Donne insists on it. His is the religious temperament, in
that he cannot content himself with the transient and the
manifold.

On a huge hill,
Cragged, and steep, Truth stands, and hee that will
Reach her, about must, and about must goe;
And what the hills suddennes resists, winne so;[1]

The immediate sense of God was not for him. Vaughan,
Blake, Francis Thompson, were seers or mystics in a sense
in which Donne never was. But he shared their desire.
Human love was not enough.

Here the admyring her my mind did whett
To seek thee God;[2]

It was not by accident that Donne turned at last to religious
poetry and to the pulpit. His direction was manifest in the
nature of his images. The poets who best understood their
intention were religious poets.

Let no pious ear be offended [writes Dr Johnson], if I advance,
in opposition to many authorities, that poetical devotion cannot
often please. The doctrines of Religion may indeed be defended
in a didactick poem, and he who has the happy power of arguing
in verse, will not lose it because his subject is sacred. A poet may
describe the beauty and grandeur of Nature, the flowers of the
Spring, and the harvests of Autumn, the vicissitudes of the Tide,
and the revolutions of the Sky, and praise the Maker for his
works in lines which no reader shall lay aside. The subject of the
disputation is not piety but the motives to piety; that of the
description is not God, but the works of God.

[1] *Satyre* III.   [2] *Holy Sonnet* XVII.

Contemplative piety, or the intercourse between God and the human soul, cannot be poetical. Man admitted to implore the mercy of his Creator, and plead the merits of his Redeemer, is already in a higher state than poetry can confer.[1]

Devotional poetry is exposed to attack both from believers like Dr Johnson and from the sceptical. Johnson rejects it because he assumes that it can add nothing to religious experience; 'religion must be shewn as it is; suppression and addition equally corrupt it; and such as it is, it is already known.'[2] Meanwhile, the unbelieving reader is baffled by the strangeness of what is offered him in devotional poetry. If religious experience means nothing to him, how can he enjoy poetry which is the expression of it? At first sight the complaints seem opposite to one another. For one the subject is too familiar, for the other it is too remote. But both spring from the same misconception. Both assign the wrong kind of importance to the subject of a poem. Poetry is not about things in the same sense in which a prose treatise is about something. A poem expresses, not the thing itself, but the poet's feeling of it. One poet is moved by religious experience, another by human love, another by the song of a bird or the sight of a flower, yet another by a political idea. It does not matter to the reader whether he himself could have been affected by that thing, but only whether the poem affects him. In *The Rambler*, no. 86, Johnson talks of the poet's power of 'joining musick with reason, and of acting at once upon the senses and the passions', in his *Life of Milton* he speaks of poetry 'calling imagination to the help of reason'. The excitement experienced by readers of poetry may be due to this sudden binding together of the whole man. The immediate result of such an experience is heightened consciousness.

Dr Johnson recognized that a poem should not leave the reader as it found him. That is the gravamen of his charge against devotional poetry, for he nowhere envisages an

[1] *Life of Waller.*   [2] Ibid.

irreligious reader. 'Watts' devotional poetry is, like that of
others, unsatisfactory, the paucity of its topicks enforces
perpetual repetition', or of Fenton's *Odes* he writes: 'As
the sentiments are pious they cannot easily be new, for
what can be added to topicks on which successive ages have
been employed?' If the answer be 'nothing', his objection
to religious poetry is valid; but it applies equally to love
poetry. The 'topicks' presented by the Christian faith are
limited, but so are the 'topicks' suggested by human love.
Successive ages have been employed about both. Yet out
of these time-worn experiences, poets are continually
creating something new. Even in our own time fresh
treasure has been dug from this mine; this for instance:

The Folly of Being Comforted.

One that is ever kind said yesterday:
'Your well-belovèd's hair has threads of grey,
And little shadows come about her eyes;
Time can but make it easier to be wise
Though now it seems impossible, and so
All that you need is patience.'
            Heart cries, 'No,
I have not a crumb of comfort, not a grain.
Time can but make her beauty over again:
Because of that great nobleness of hers
The fire that stirs about her, when she stirs,
Burns but more clearly. O she had not these ways
When all the wild summer was in her gaze.'

O heart! O heart! if she'd but turn her head,
You'd know the folly of being comforted.[1]

The distinction is not in the theme, other poets have written
about a loved woman growing old. A wistful little poem
of Hardy's will serve for comparison:

Wives in the Sere.

Never a careworn wife but shows,
    If a joy suffuse her,

[1] W. B. Yeats.

Something beautiful to those
    Patient to peruse her,
Some one charm the world unknows
    Precious to a muser,
Haply what, ere years were foes,
    Moved her mate to choose her.

But, be it a hint of rose
    That an instant hues her,
Or some early light or pose
    Wherewith thought renews her—
Seen by him at full, ere woes
    Practised to abuse her—
Sparely comes it, swiftly goes,
    Time again subdues her.

It is no more than the subject of the two poems that is similar. In its development Yeats combines the loss with the gain; there is no comfort for what is lost; there is no need for comfort, because of what is gained. Hardy lays stress, characteristically, on the cruelty of time and on human tenderness. Even this single aspect of the experience of love, the ageing of the beloved, can be felt and expressed in countless ways. Donne expressed it in *Elegie* IX. *The Autumnal.*

The love of God takes as many different forms, and gives rise to as many different states of mind, as the love of woman. The same beliefs or circumstances produce unendingly varying effects. The fear that poets inspired by Christian beliefs will merely repeat what is already known to the Christian reader need not be seriously entertained, though it may be replaced by the fear, valid for all kinds of poetry, that the reader will take nothing from the poem but what he brought to it.

A more debatable point in our day is, whether there will be any common ground between the religious poet and a reader who has no share in Christian beliefs. The possibility of communication between poet and reader depends upon there being something in common between them. Fortunately for poetry human needs and impulses are recurrent, though the directions in which satisfaction is sought are very varied. The state of mind in such a poem as Francis Thompson's *The Hound of Heaven* is readily conveyed to an unbeliever, although it may have no exact parallel in his experience. The poem itself, with its abundant imagery and insistent rhythm, can communicate it:

> I fled Him, down the nights and down the days;
> I fled Him, down the arches of the years;
> I fled Him, down the labyrinthine ways
> Of my own mind; and in the mist of tears
> I hid from Him, and under running laughter.
> Up vistaed hopes I sped;
> And shot, precipitated,
> Adown Titanic glooms of chasmèd fears,
> From those strong Feet that followed, followed after.
> But with unhurrying chase,
> And unperturbèd pace,
> Deliberate speed, majestic instancy,
> They beat—and a Voice beat
> More instant than the Feet—
> 'All things betray thee, who betrayest Me'.

The impulse to escape from the unknown, and the longing to be at one with it, the hurry of thought to avoid contemplation, the fear of paying too great a price for what is most desired:

> (For, though I knew His love Who followèd,
> Yet was I sore adread
> Lest, having Him, I must have nought beside.)

these conflicting impulses are sufficiently common to be intelligible in the guise in which Francis Thompson's faith clothes them. The poem, like Herbert's *Affliction*, is a biography of the human spirit, its adventures may be strange, but the adventurer is familiar. This is likely to be always the case. Poets are rare, but this does not mean that they are different in kind from their readers, they are different in their degree of awareness, their power of co-ordinating experiences, and, chiefly of course, in the nature and degree of their command of words. For a reader of devotional poetry, as of any other kind, the most important qualification is responsiveness to the language and rhythms of poetry. He need not share the poet's beliefs, he may even be more responsive, because more flexible and unreserved, less tempted to foist his own experience on to the poem, if he does not: but he must be susceptible to the poet's power to recreate experience.

Suppose a reader, sensitive to poetry, but repelled by or indifferent to the doctrine of the resurrection of the body, reads Gerard Manley Hopkins' poem, *The Caged Skylark*.

As a dare-gale skylark scanted in a dull cage
    Man's mounting spirit in his bone-house, mean house, dwells—
    That bird beyond the remembering his free fells;
This in drudgery, day-labouring-out life's age.

Though aloft on turf or perch or poor low stage,
    Both sing sometimes the sweetest, sweetest spells,
    Yet both droop deadly sómetimes in their cells
Or wring their barriers in bursts of fear or rage.

Not that the sweet-fowl, song-fowl, needs no rest—
Why, hear him, hear him babble and drop down to his nest,
    But his own nest, wild nest, no prison.
Man's spirit will be flesh-bound when found at best,
But uncumbered: meadow-down is not distressed
    For a rainbow footing it nor he for his bónes rísen.

The poem does not convert such a reader to the doctrine implied, in the sense in which a theological treatise might conceivably do so. And yet in some sense the thought and feeling in the poem are transferred to him. There is again something in common between poet and reader to begin with. There can be few who have not felt the body to be both prison and home, both encumbrance and delight, both an insufferable limitation and a centre of rest and refreshment. Such a background of common experience is all that is needed. The poem does the rest. Hopkins more even than most poets repays close attention to his verbal pattern. His words are like pieces in a mosaic, he composes with these fragments. This particular poem is built up in a series of contrasts, the harsh thuds of the prison motif 'scanted in a dull cage'; 'in his bone-house, mean house, dwells—'; 'This in drudgery, day-labouring-out life's age'; 'Or wring their barriers in bursts of fear or rage'; contrasted with the open, liquid sound of the free-flight motif: 'Man's mounting spirit'; 'remembering his free fells'; 'Both sing sometimes the sweetest, sweetest spells'; 'Why, hear him, hear him babble and drop down to his nest'; 'meadow-down is not distressed For a rainbow footing it nor he for his bónes rísen'. Finally the reader possesses, not Hopkins' belief, but his feeling of what it would be like to meet the body again in its resurrected state. Acquaintance with the doctrine concerning the resurrection of the body is necessary for the poem to be understood, particularly the line which is nearest to prose statement:

> Man's spirit will be flesh-bound when found at best,
> But uncumbered:

but most poetry requires some familiarity with the tradition from which it springs. English poetry, secular or sacred, has its roots in European culture, with its inheritance of Greek, Latin, Hebrew and Christian literatures, the ideas they embody and the gods they celebrate. Given two readers of equal sensibility the more widely read has always an advantage.

Dr Johnson raised one more objection to devotional poetry which suggests other issues than the familiarity or strangeness of religious experience. 'The ideas of Christian Theology are', he writes, 'too simple for eloquence, too sacred for fiction, and too majestic for ornament; to recommend them by tropes and figures, is to magnify by a concave mirror the sidereal hemisphere.'[1] This assertion is

[1] *Life of Waller.*

based upon two assumptions, one concerning the means and the other the ends of poetry. In the first place it assumes that poetry is necessarily eloquence; that it achieves its effects by heightening or, as Johnson puts it, 'by tropes and figures' which 'magnify'. He rarely talks nonsense and here, as almost always with him, an important truth is embodied in the questionable verdict. Certain human experiences are beyond eloquence; they can only be expressed with the utmost simplicity. There comes a moment in great tragedy when grandeur of diction, violence of imagery, magnificence of verse can do no more. They give place to unadorned statement:

> Do not laugh at me;
> For, as I am a man, I think this lady
> To be my child Cordelia.

The ecstasy of religious experience, like the height of tragedy, is beyond the reach of oratory. Verbal elaboration can but travesty such moments; poets use other means. Even Milton, most magniloquent of poets, can lay aside his singing robes, for example, in the closing lines of the sonnet *On his deceased wife*:

> Her face was veiled; yet to my fancied sight
> Love, sweetness, goodness, in her person shined
> So clear as in no face with more delight.
> But oh! as to embrace me she inclined,
> I waked, she fled, and day brought back my night.

He uses no eloquence to bewail his blindness. The bare statements 'her face was veiled', 'and day brought back my night', are enough. Again, no attempt at description could achieve the effect of Vaughan's

> I saw Eternity the other night;[1]

no elaborate words could convey the serene joy of Blake's simple statement:

[1] *The World.*

The moon like a flower
In heaven's high bower,
With silent delight
Sits and smiles on the night.[1]

The pinnacle of joy or of sorrow can only be treated in
poetry when the poet denies himself his ordinary aids. All
the verbal tricks that enhance or inflate a theme are set
aside, economy of statement is more moving:

There a very little girth
Can hold round what once the earth
Seemed too narrow to contain.[2]

Dr Johnson is right in discerning that some human experiences (and for him religious experience is the type of
these) will bear no elaboration. He may have been in-
sensitive to the undertones of poetry, as he was to those
of prose (witness his criticisms of Swift). But this is not all.
His stricture implies, not only that poetry has no means
with which to deal with such experience; but also that it
is unworthy of the office. He has in mind a clear conception
of what religion is and of what poetry is, and he sets the
one beyond the reach of the other. The difficulty here is
that the modern commentator cannot meet Dr Johnson
on his own ground. The words poetry and religion
comprehend so many kinds of experience, that they no
longer seem susceptible of definition, indeed Johnson himself admitted that 'to circumscribe poetry by a definition'
could 'only show the narrowness of the definer'.[3] How
then is it to be compared with that other elusive experience,
religion? Only, probably, by considering, not what either
is in itself, but what effects they produce in those who
experience them. Poetry and religion each exert power over
those who are sensitive to them. There may be fields in
which religion operates and poetry does not, as there may
be areas of the mind affected by poetry and untouched by

[1] *Songs of Innocence, Night*.   [2] Christina Rossetti, *The Bourne*.
[3] *Life of Pope*.

faith. But over certain areas both operate. Either can quicken sensibility; either can impose an order upon scattered thoughts and feelings. From one point of view love, or religion, or the beauty of nature can be thought of as materials for poetry, but from another, from that which considers their effects, they can be thought of as commensurable with it. The poet's power over the subtle and complex meanings of words suggests the possibility of perfection, just as the beloved does to the lover or religion to the believer:

> So in a voice, so in a shapelesse flame
> Angels affect us oft and worshipped be.[1]

[1] *Aire and Angels.*

BIBLIOGRAPHICAL NOTE

A valuable introduction to seventeenth-century metaphysical poetry is to be found in the essay introductory to

Metaphysical Lyrics and Poems of the Seventeenth Century. Selected and edited, with an Essay, by H. J. C. GRIERSON (Oxford, Clarendon Press, 1921);

and in two Essays by Mr T. S. ELIOT:

The Metaphysical Poets and *Andrew Marvell*, first published in 1924 in *Homage to John Dryden* (Hogarth Press), and since reissued in *Selected Essays* (Faber and Faber, 1932).

For fuller bibliographical guidance consult *English Literature in the Earlier Seventeenth Century, 1600–1660*, by DOUGLAS BUSH (Oxford History of English Literature, vol. v, Second Edition, 1963), pp. 565–9.

The standard editions of the five poets are:

The Poems of John Donne. Edited by H. J. C. GRIERSON. 2 vols. Clarendon Press, 1912.

The Works of George Herbert. Edited with a Commentary by F. E. HUTCHINSON. Clarendon Press, 1941.

The Works of Henry Vaughan. Edited by L. C. MARTIN. 2 vols. Clarendon Press, 1914.

The Poems, English, Latin and Greek, of Richard Crashaw. Edited by L. C. MARTIN. Clarendon Press, 1927.

The Poems and Letters of Andrew Marvell. Edited by H. M. MARGOLIOUTH. 2 vols. Clarendon Press, 1927.

Professor Grierson's text of Donne's poems is almost exactly reproduced in

John Donne, Dean of St Paul's, Complete Poetry and Selected Prose. Edited by JOHN HAYWARD (The Nonesuch Press, 1929). This volume also contains a representative selection of Donne's letters in prose and verse.

INDEX